Th

25.–

Pleuropneumonia-Like Organisms (PPLO)
Mycoplasmataceae

# Pleuropneumonia-Like Organisms (PPLO) Mycoplasmataceae

E. KLIENEBERGER-NOBEL

*Lister Institute of Preventive Medicine, London*

1962

ACADEMIC PRESS

LONDON and NEW YORK

ACADEMIC PRESS INC. (LONDON) LTD.
17 Old Queen Street
London, S.W.1.


U.S. Edition published by
ACADEMIC PRESS INC.
111 FIFTH AVENUE
NEW YORK 3, NEW YORK

*Library of Congress Catalog Number: 61–17505*


Printed in the Netherlands by
JOH. ENSCHEDÉ EN ZONEN GRAFISCHE INRICHTING N.V.

# PREFACE

This book provides information on a group of organisms called pleuropneumonia-like organisms (PPLO), or Mycoplasmataceae (Edward and Freundt, 1956). For convenience the abbreviation "PPLO" is here used throughout. PPLO have for a long time been regarded as a "freak of nature" of minor importance and have therefore been neglected by the majority of medical and scientific bacteriologists. The veterinarians, of course, could not by-pass them since some ravaging diseases of domestic animals are caused by members of the group.

However, in the last 10–20 years it has emerged that PPLO are widely distributed in nature; some are saprophytes and have been found in sewage and soil, others are parasites and aetiological agents of disease. Two very severe epizootics causing considerable economic losses are caused by members of the PPLO group, one a lung disease of cattle and goats, the other a mastitis (and sometimes a systemic disease) in sheep and goats. Small laboratory animals suffer from lung, joint and brain diseases of PPLO origin; the organisms may be present in these rodents in a latent state and may be "lit up" when the animals are operated upon or subjected to some other experimental stress. Moreover certain pathological conditions in dogs, goats, cattle and pigs are suspected to be of PPLO aetiology. Human beings also seem to be subject to PPLO infections some of which are probably venereal in nature; such severe conditions as abacterial haemorrhagic cystitis and abacterial salpingitis are believed to be caused by a particular PPLO.

It has further been shown that PPLO may occur as admixtures in strains of bacteria and *Trichomonas vaginalis* and in tissue cultures, all of which have primarily been regarded as pure cultures. If these contaminations are not discovered, they may adversely affect the results of experiments.

The organisms of the pleuropneumonia group are a special class of microbe with unique characteristics and all members of the group are closely related. They do not possess rigid cell walls as do most other microorganisms. Consequently, they are of a soft and plastic nature and produce cells of various sizes and shapes. These cells are delicate and unsubstantial and can easily be deformed and destroyed. They produce very small granules, each of which is able to reproduce on artificial media the characteristic minute colony.

For these reasons they are distinct from bacteria as well as from viruses, and thus may have their place between these two groups of agents. Intense studies have already given valuable information on the morphology, immunology and pathogenicity of these organisms. Their physiology, nutrition and metabolism have also been investigated. However, in all these fields only a beginning has been made so far and further studies will be necessary for a better understanding of this group of microbes.

In the following chapters, the available knowledge in the various fields is presented as far as it is considered to be of importance, the special methods that have been applied to the studies of these organisms are described, and an attempt is made to resolve some of the bewildering controversial opinions on their nature.

It is the main purpose of this book to introduce bacteriologists who are newcomers, to some of the practical and theoretical aspects of the subject which may enable them to embark on successful research in this long neglected, but important and interesting, field.

With regard to controversial matters, I have given my own points of view which are the outcome of many years of studies and observations.

Dr. S. Razin, The Hebrew University, Hadassah Medical School, Jerusalem, Israel has contributed a valuable chapter on the "Nutrition and Metabolism of the PPLO".

July, 1961.

# CONTENTS

# CHAPTER I

# The Great Epizootics, Bovine Pleuropneumonia and Agalactia of Sheep and Goats and the Discovery of their Aetiological Agents

## A. CONTAGIOUS PLEUROPNEUMONIA BOVIS

### 1. *The Disease*

Pleuropneumonia bovis is one of the scourges of animal husbandry involving enormous losses. About the spread of the disease we read in a paper by Tang *et al.* (1935): "According to Foster (1934) it first appeared in Switzerland and Germany in 1713 and in England in 1735. By the end of the 18th century it had spread over the entire German empire, France and Italy. It was carried from England to Australia in 1858 and about the same time from Holland to South Africa. At present the disease is distributed widely throughout the world with the exception of most of Europe, and North America. The United States of America was affected in 1843 and it was only by the most energetic and rigid government veterinary measures that the disease was finally eradicated. The history of pleuropneumonia in China is very obscure. As far as we are aware the first outbreak occurred in 1919 when the disease was discovered in a Shanghai dairy, having been introduced by a shipment of milk cows from Australia. In 1920 Hongkong was also reported to be infected from the same source. In 1931 Shanghai was reinvaded by the disease. Since its introduction pleuropneumonia has become endemic in Shanghai and has gradually invaded neighbouring areas such as Kiangwan, Woosung, Pootung, etc. . . ."

The eradication of the disease in North America was a great achievement and one of the rules then introduced is still in force; namely, a ban on the introduction of cultures of the organism of pleuropneumonia bovis into the country. Hence American bacteriologists have no opportunity of studying this organism in their laboratories.

From the "Animal Health Yearbook" of 1957 published by the "Food and Agricultural Organisation of the United Nations" (F.A.O.) and the "Office Internationale des Epizooties" (O.I.E.) the following information on world distribution is obtained: Spain seems to be the only country of Europe in which pleuropneumonia still occurs in both cattle and goats although the number of animals developing the condition is small and the disease is confined to certain regions*.

*It should be pointed out here that pleuropneumonia of cattle and pleuropneumonia of goats are similar diseases caused by two closely related but not identical organisms, which in turn are different from the organism of agalactia in goats and sheep.

1

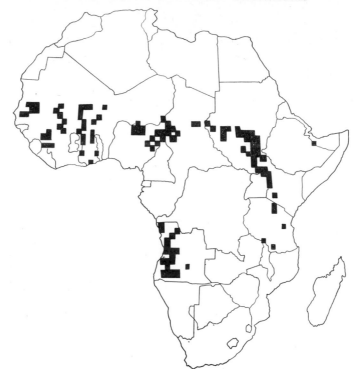

FIG. 1.  Geographical distribution map on contagious bovine pleuropneumonia in Africa south of the Sahara, 1956. (Reproduced from *Bulletin of Epizootic Diseases of Africa*, **5**, 207, 1957).

FIG. 2.  Areas of Australia where contagious bovine pleuropneumonia is enzootic. (Reproduced from *Commonwealth of Australia Service Publications* No. 10; "Diseases of Domestic Animals in Australia", Part 5, Vol. II, (1953). Bacterial Diseases, by H. R. Seddon, opposite page 376.)

Pleuropneumonia of cattle does not occur in the countries of the Near East although pleuropneumonia of goats is widespread in Turkey and Iran and also occurs at a low incidence or confined to certain areas in Iraq and Afghanistan.

In India pleuropneumonia of goats is widespread, whereas pleuropneumonia of cattle is confined to certain regions only. Both pleuropneumonia of cattle and pleuropneumonia of goats occur at a low incidence in Pakistan.

FIG. 3. Main lines of spread of contagious bovine pleuropneumonia from original focus near Melbourne. (Reproduced from *Commonwealth of Australia Service Publications*, No. 10: "Diseases of Domestic Animals in Australia", Part 5, Vol. II (1953). Bacterial Diseases, by H. R. Seddon, opposite page 366.)

Africa and Australia are the two continents in which pleuropneumonia of cattle is still epizootic; it is widespread in the Sudan, Somaliland, French West Africa, Ethiopia, and occurs in certain regions in Nigeria, Tanganyika and Kenya. Pleuropneumonia of goats is also epizootic in some of these countries. Figure 1 shows the distribution of pleuropneumonia of cattle in Africa south of the Sahara*.

---

* I should like to quote a remark in a recent letter from the Director of the Interafrican Bureau for Animal Health (W. G. Beaton, Muguga, Kenya): " . . . a later distribution map is not available . . . there has been quite a marked reduction of the incidence in most of the enzootic territories . . . . the map refers only to the territories of Africa which are members of the Commission for Technical Cooperation in Africa south of the Sahara and . . . Ethiopia which is known to be infected is not indicated as an enzootic area."

Pleuropneumonia of cattle will probably be an unsolved problem for years to come in Australia. It is epizootic in the North and in certain regions of Queensland, from which area it can still be introduced into the now "clean" regions of the south and west, although due to very rigid control measures it can no longer establish itself there. The situation in 1953 is seen from Fig. 2, Seddon (1953).

The records of the introduction of pleuropneumonia bovis into various parts of Australia, its spread, and the measures for its final successful control in the south and west, make a fascinating and instructive story. Our account follows the chapter on "Contagious bovine pleuropneumonia" in "Diseases of Domestic Animals in Australia" by H. R. Seddon (1953). As seen from Fig. 3 the disease appeared first near Melbourne in Victoria in 1858. From there it spread rapidly to New South Wales, South Australia and Queensland. It moved along the Sidney Road with "mobs on the hoof" and "working bullock teams" used for transport of merchandise. About 1880 the disease had established itself as an epizootic plague in the Northern Territory and in 1897 the first cases were recorded in Western Australia near Perth. The disease was introduced into Perth and into Wyndham in the high North through cattle conveyed by ship. In the western part of North Australia the infection was first noted in 1928.

Today pleuropneumonia bovis is enzootic only in the north of Australia, an area lying within the tropics, and parts of Queensland, particularly the "channel country." Across the large plains of this area the water spreads through a series of channels when the rivers become swollen through the heavy rains of northern Queensland. Here the cattle stations are very extensive. Nearly three million cattle are kept in the large holdings of these epizootic areas, feed is good, and movements of the animals are uncontrolled. The properties are unfenced and the half-wild animals roam widely; once or twice a year the cattle from these large herds are segregated for the markets but since it is impractical to muster all the animals it is impossible to estimate the incidence of the disease and to fulfil the first prerogative of control, namely the slaughter of all diseased cattle. For reasons of animal husbandry the mustered animals from the infected areas are introduced into western and southern areas for fattening, from where they go to the abattoirs as "fats." Thus pleuropneumonia breaks out intermittently and sporadically in the "clean areas" and only through rigid control measures do dairy herds and breeding stock remain free from the disease in these regions.

As can be imagined economic losses have been very high in the past. They are still high even in the clean districts because of restrictions imposed on stock movement and because of the large number of people and apparatus necessary to impose measures of control such as slaughter, serological field tests, and vaccination. The following may give an indication of losses involved: An estimate made in 1873 puts down the total Australian losses up to that year at about 1,400,000 head of cattle, a total value of £ 8,500,000 or approximately of £ 6 per head.

For a long time control measures were not very effective because the disease was not properly understood and even its infectivity was doubted before the discovery of the organism in 1898. Symptoms are extremely variable: in experimental infections (now induced by a heavy spray of a virulent culture causing droplet infection) half the animals show only mild or subclinical symptoms and the same happens with naturally infected beasts. Cattle which are actually ill may show all or some of the following symptoms: (1) fever; (2) respiratory symptoms (rapid shallow breathing); (3) soft cough, nasal discharge; (4) preference to stand with extension of head; (5) drooped ears, rough coat, sunken eyes; (6) general poor condition. However, chronically diseased or latently infected cattle may not show any symptoms, in fact in seemingly healthy animals sequestra may be present for many months with the organism still alive in them; these asymptomatic animals endanger the healthy stock. There was no possibility of diagnosing their infection before the introduction of the complement fixation test in 1936 (Campbell and Turner). Since that time field tests have been carried out and the positive reacters found and slaughtered. Another great advance in control was achieved when, at about the same time, a standard culture vaccine (consisting of viable but not too virulent organisms) was introduced for the immunisation of healthy animals. Two-tenths of a ml. of this vaccine is injected about one inch from the tip of the tail. The local reaction may commence about the second or third day after inoculation as a very slight swelling but more often is delayed until the fifth or sixth day. By the seventh day there is usually a well marked oedematous swelling extending for two or three inches up from the tip of the tail. It is interesting to note that following the inoculation a mild systemic reaction usually occurs with organisms appearing in the blood stream. Vaccinated calves frequently develop polyarthritis.

When vaccinated animals were challenged by exposure to a large quantity of nebulized culture it was found that only 3% were not influenced by vaccination, the others had developed various degrees of immunity and when resistance was produced it persisted for long periods. It is of interest and importance to know that careful examination of many strains has shown that only one immunological type of pleuropneumonia bovis organism exists in Australia and probably there is only one strain in the whole world.

The main control measures which at present keep the clean areas of Australia free from reinfection are the following: Slaughter of all clinically diseased and serologically positive animals; vaccination of all healthy cattle which have to be certified as being of clean stock; in the event of disease, the follow up of contacts, the elimination of the source of infection; notification of diseased animals and prohibition of entry.

## 2. *The Agent*

The discoverers of the organism causing pleuropneumonia in cattle were the famous French workers Nocard and Roux who, together with their collaborators Borrel, Salimbeni and Dujardin-Beaumetz, described the disease and its cause in 1898. As this very infectious and often fatal cattle plague was at that time still enzootic in Europe these workers had first hand information about the pathology and course of the disease and their classical description is well worth mentioning. They pointed out that the main pathological feature of pleuropneumonia bovis is an enormous extension of the interlobar connective tissue which contains a serous, albuminous, yellowish and clear exudate. This liquid is very virulent. If a drop is injected subcutaneously into a cow the animal develops fever and an extensive oedema containing litres of serous fluid spreading over the rump, the legs or the tail region of the animal according to the place of injection. Under these circumstances the "virus" never enters the pleural cavity, nor does it invade the lungs. The condition thus produced may be serious or even fatal or it may eventually resolve itself. In the latter case the animal becomes immune against natural or experimental infection. When injection into the tail of the animal is practised according to Willems of Hasselt, Belgium (1900) — still the method of choice for purposes of vaccination — the inflammation and the temperature remain moderate as a rule, but resistance usually develops.

As the French authors suspected a living agent to be the cause of the disease, but were not able to demonstrate bacteria in the exudate, they resorted to a method devised by Metchnikoff, Roux and Salimbeni (1896); they inserted into the peritoneal cavity of a rabbit, a collodion sac filled with broth inoculated with a drop of exudate. After a period varying between a few days and some months the animal was killed and it was found that the inoculated sac contained an opalescent, virulent liquid but no bacteria, whereas uninoculated control sacs were filled with a clear, nonvirulent liquid. Although rabbits cannot be infected with the agent of pleuropneumonia the animals lost a considerable amount of weight and were emaciated; similar results could not be obtained with guinea-pigs. The authors concluded that the agent had multiplied in the collodion sac protected against the defence mechanism of the body, utilizing at the same time nutrients provided by the animal. They pointed out further that whereas the agent was retained in the sac its toxic products diffused through and this accounted for the deterioration of the animal's general condition and particularly loss of its weight.

Spurred on by the success of these experiments, the authors soon learned to grow the agent of bovine pleuropneumonia in Martin's broth ("System of Bacteriology", Vol. 9, 1931) enriched with serum. In this medium it developed so slightly that the authors advised comparison of the inoculated and incubated tubes with sterile ones in order to detect the turbidity, a practice that can still be recommended.

In 1900 Dujardin-Beaumetz gave a good description of the growth of the organism of pleuropneumonia bovis (*Mycoplasma mycoides*, Edward and Freundt, 1956) on solid medium. He published photographs of the small colonies with their characteristic dark centre and their lighter periphery and one of his pictures of a colony section illustrates the central growth embedding itself into the medium.

Ten years later the first detailed description of the morphology of the organism of pleuropneumonia bovis, including staining procedures, were published by Bordet (1910) and by Borrel, Dujardin-Beaumetz Jeantet and Jouan (1910). Improved modern methods have revealed so much of the peculiar morphology and the development of the organism that there is now a much better understanding of it than was possible at the time of the publication of the above mentioned papers. Methods for the demonstration of the morphology, growth and isolation of the organism of pleuropneumonia bovis and related microbes will be described in Chapters III and IV.

## B. Infectious Agalactia of Sheep and Goats

### 1. *The Disease*

Agalactia of sheep and goats manifests itself mainly in the lambing season when the females should be in milk; instead they produce a purulent secretion. This disease, known in Italy under the name of "Stornarella", was first described by Metaxa (1816) as follows: "The Stornarella is a chronic and contagious disease in the course of which the milk is transformed into a salty liquid of bluish appearance. Usually the animals cure themselves, but sometimes the eyes become involved which results in blindness."* In 1871 Brusasco gave it the name "infectious agalactia of sheep and goats". Before the end of the century it had become enzootic in many countries of Europe.

* Translated from the French by the author from Zavagli's paper of 1951.

As Zavagli (1951) points, out the disease is not localized, but generalized and systemic although the main economic loss comes from mammary, ocular or synovial infection.

## (a)  *The Mammary Lesions*

The agent produces in the lactating female a catarrhalic or parenchymatic mastitis; milk secretion stops and either a viscous purulent discharge appears or the milk becomes watery and divides itself into two layers, an upper of grey-bluish appearance and a lower with a sediment of yellow-green granules. The mammary tissue becomes flabby and shrinks, and hard nodules develop. In the beginning the alkalinity of the milk increases and numerous leucocytes appear in the secretion; germs demonstrable by ordinary bacteriological methods are not found. When the animals finally recover their quarters are permanently damaged, a great economic loss.

## (b)  *The Eye Lesions*

When the disease is severe it effects females, males and lambs in the same way, i.e. parenchymatous keratitis or panophthalmia develops. Eventually, a rupture of the cornea may take place, and the various constituents of the eye are expelled with resultant blindness.

## (c)  *The Joint Lesions*

The legs are mainly affected, the joints swell and become oedematous and purulent and sometimes there are abscesses which rupture. Eventually arthritis and ankylosis develop and in very severe cases the animals become wasted and can no longer stand upright.

In the course of the disease certain alterations occur in the blood. Zavagli reports that the number of monocytes in the blood is considerably increased and simultaneously a decrease in the number of leucocytes occurs.

## 2.  *The Agent*

The causative agent of agalactia can remain alive in the dung for a considerable time and as a result herds can become infected in localities (stables, enclosures) previously occupied by infected animals; the agent enters the system by means of the digestive tract. It is assumed that the animals acquire a potential infection that can remain latent at least for several months until the right conditions, such as fatigue, parturition or lactation, cause a breakdown of resistance.

Celli and De Blasi (1906) were the first to show that agalactia is caused by an agent that passes filters which retain bacteria. In 1923 and 1925 Bridré and Donatien reported that they had achieved the successful culture of the agent on serum agar and in liquid medium and could infect lactating animals with the cultivated organism. They also showed the filterability of the culture through "L bis" candles and gave the first description of the colony type on solid medium as follows: After three to four days incubation, very small, transparent, hardly visible colonies develop which adhere strongly to the medium. Under low power magnification these colonies appear as opaque nipples surrounded by clearer zones. This type of colony is the same as that produced by the organism of pleuropneumonia bovis.

Zavagli reports that an experimental infection establishes itself when the organisms are injected subcutaneously into the armpit of lactating sheep. He has observed that they appear in the blood stream between the twelfth and twenty-fourth hour after the inoculation. After 36 hours the organisms have disappeared from the blood and have reached the organs of predilection. After 24 hours the organisms may be present in the milk and on the second day they appear in abundance in the spleen. They are not found in the kidney but may be present in the brain.

The preventive method of choice is vaccination of healthy animals. Zavagli uses two types of vaccine in succession: first a vaccine is used consisting of milk rich in organisms and inactivated with formol, followed by a vaccine prepared by extracting the agent from infected tissues, adsorbing on to aluminium hydroxide and attenuating by heat and formol. From experiments carried out with large numbers of sheep Zavagli concluded that 100% immunisation can be obtained by vaccination. However, the various "viruses" are not identical and therefore the vaccine has to be prepared in different regions by local Institutes. This is, as Zavagli points out, a great drawback which has to be overcome by proper organisation. Zavagli's interesting investigations have so far not been repeated by other workers.

Information about the present distribution of agalactia in the various countries of the world is given in the 1957 "Animal Health Yearbook" published by F.A.O. and O.I.E. In many countries of Europe and the Near East agalactia of sheep and goats is still found. It occurs at a low incidence or is confined to certain regions in the Netherlands, France, Switzerland, Austria, Hungary, Italy, Spain, Jugoslavia, Rumania, Greece, Syria, Jordan, Lebanon and Israel, whereas it is widespread in Turkey and Iran.

Agalactia of sheep and goats is not enzootic in the south of Africa, but occurs at a low incidence or confined to certain areas in such northern countries as Morocco, Algeria, Tunisia, Tripolitania and in the Sudan.

Agalactia is not very widespread in the Far East, Oceania or America. It is found at a low incidence in India and it is thought to occur in Paraguay. Some caprine and ovine agalactia exists in Canada.

# CHAPTER II

# The Discovery of Organisms Closely Related to the Organisms of Pleuropneumonia Bovis and Agalactia of Sheep and Goats

## A. ORGANISMS FROM DOGS WITH DISTEMPER

Before the early thirties of the present century veterinary surgeons were those most interested in the two above mentioned epizootics and their aetiological causes. During the thirties a slightly wider circle of workers started to take an interest in the organisms of the pleuropneumonia group. This was probably the reason why, in the following ten years, a number of new organisms closely related to those causing pleuropneumonia in cattle were discovered. Ledingham, who in 1933 published a study on the morphology of the only two organisms then known, wrote, with reference to the discovery of the organism of agalactia, ". . . it is indeed fortunate from the point of view of systematic morphology that the pleuropneumonia organism no longer occupies an isolated position." At that very time Shoetensack (1934, 1936 a, b) in Tokyo was studying canine distemper. On solid culture media he grew from the nasal secretion, lung and liver of a number of dogs, a "filterable virus" which, as he pointed out, resembled in colony type and morphology the organism of pleuropneumonia of cattle. He used a glucose blood medium and cultured two types of organisms which he found more difficult to grow than the organism of pleuropneumonia. Indeed they are more exacting, as the present author, to whom he sent his cultures, can confirm. They did however grow quite well on a "boiled blood horse serum agar" (Klieneberger, 1938). Shoetensack believed that they might be the cause of canine distemper. We know now, largely through Laidlaw's work, that this disease is caused by a true virus. However, Shoetensack's organisms cultivated from nasal secretion and lung of dogs ill with distemper, may well have had an aggravating effect on this condition. We do not know if they occur regularly in cases of distemper, or if they are pathogens or saprophytes, since nobody has ever repeated Shoetensack's work.

## B. SAPROPHYTIC ORGANISMS

In 1936 Laidlaw and Elford published a paper on "a new group of filterable organisms" obtained by filtration of raw sewage through "gradocol" membranes (Elford, 1931). They found that these organisms grew well on Hartley's digest broth, (Mackie and McCartney, 1959) enriched with Fildes' peptic digest of red cells (Mackie and

McCartney, 1959) and adjusted to a pH of approximately 8.0. Growth in liquid media occurred as a fine haze which developed into a slight turbidity. The optimum temperature of growth was 30°C. The colonies are described as "umbonate" with a rough brownish centre and a flatter smoother periphery sometimes with radial markings. When well isolated and incubated for five to six days they may reach 0·35 mm. in diameter. Laidlaw and Elford point out "it is possible to count the number of viable organisms in a fluid culture by plating a known volume of an appropriate dilution on to solid medium, incubating for four or five days and counting the separate colonies under a low power binocular microscope." It will thus be found that a clear medium may contain 40 million organisms per ml. and a slightly turbid culture medium from 3 to 10 thousand million organisms per ml.

Laidlaw and Elford determined the generation time during the logarithmic growth phase of strain "A" to be 1·6 hours at 30°C on the assumption that the organism multiplied by simple fission. However, from their observations they regarded it as improbable that multiplication of the large forms occurred by this means. As will be shown in Chapter III this observation was correct. Laidlaw and Elford discovered three types of saprophytic strains, "A", "B", and "C" which, although distinct serologically, showed similar morphology, with elements described as globular, disk-shaped and granular, the latter so small that they cannot be properly resolved under the ordinary microscope. They were shown to be present in the cultures by filtration experiments in which it was found that the least porous membrane that still yielded a positive filtrate had an average pore diameter (A.P.D.) of 0·26 μ. The filtration end point thus coincided with that previously found by Elford and Andrewes (1932) for vaccinia virus. The smallest phase of the organism has, according to Elford's formula (Elford, 1938), a diameter of 125 to 175 mμ. A considerable number of elements of larger sizes, up to 0·5μ diameter are retained by the filter membranes. In their filtration behaviour, Laidlaw and Elford's sewage organisms resemble the organisms of pleuropneumonia and agalactia but they all differ from true viruses and bacteriophages by their great diversity in particle size, although each particle, large or small, can give rise to new growth. The authors end their discussion with the following stimulating remark: "Our study has shown again that organisms at least as small as the vaccinia virus, can lead an independent existence and that small size alone cannot account for our failure to cultivate any of the viruses on artificial media."

A year after the publication of Laidlaw and Elford's paper, Seiffert (1937a, b) reported that he had isolated about 30 strains of filterable organisms from various samples of soil, compost and liquid manure. From his description it is obvious that he cultivated microbes which are closely related to the sewage organisms of Laidlaw and Elford's. Klieneberger (1940) who examined six of Seiffert's and five of Laidlaw and Elford's strains confirmed this and showed by agglutination tests that Seiffert's strains were similar to Laidlaw and Elford's type "A" organism and related to the type "B", whereas Laidlaw's type "C" seemed to represent a special species.

In contrast to the organisms from pleuropneumonia and agalactia, the organisms from soil, compost and sewage seem to be saprophytes. Laidlaw and Elford had not been able to infect any of the small laboratory animals with their strains and Klieneberger-Nobel (1954) showed in experimental mixed infections that Mooser's virulence enhancing agent, ectromelia, was not instrumental in enabling them to grow in the peritoneal cavity of the mouse (see Chapter X).

## C.   Organisms from Small Laboratory Animals

During the fourth decade of this century a number of PPLO were isolated for the first time from small laboratory animals. Most of these organisms proved to be pathogens or at least potential pathogens. Some of the diseases they cause have been studied extensively and the story of the discovery of these organisms and the course of the corresponding diseases is revealing and instructive. Although the various PPLO diseases follow different patterns, there are certain striking similarities so that the study of one disease can help us to understand the others. For these reasons I shall report in greater detail on some of the PPLO diseases of small rodents.

It has been known for a long time that laboratory rats, as well as wild ones frequently show lung lesions and that this condition is widely known as bronchiectasis or bronchopneumonia. Many people have tried to grow organisms from these lesions, but the variety of bacteria obtained could not be associated with the disease. In 1937, Klieneberger and Steabben described a pleuropneumonia-like organism which they found 17 times in the lung lesions of 19 rats with bronchopneumonia when using special media for the isolations; this organism was not found in very young rats with lungs of normal appearance.

In a second paper Klieneberger and Steabben (1940) showed that the isolated PPLO was closely associated with the lung lesions of rats. They found that the disease occurred either as a chronic or an acute condition and the PPLO was always present. Stock rats developed the chronic form when ageing and were often affected between the sixth and the tenth month of their lifetime while all rats developed the condition when they reached old age at about two years. However, when under stress, for example when operated upon or when exposed to low temperature, rats can develop the disease in the acute form, becoming seriously ill and dying within a week. The sequence of events in the affected lung is described as follows by Klieneberger and Steabben (1937): ". . . first a greater secretion on the part of the epithelium of the bronchioles results in the presence of a small quantity of mucus in the lumen. This secretion actively increases and the columnar cells of the epithelium begin to proliferate. A severe peribronchial lymphocytic infiltration takes place at the same time. Later the bronchioles become distended with accumulation of mucus, and the surrounding alveoli are correspondingly atelectatic, partly owing to the mechanical pressure of the enlarging bronchioles, and partly to the failure of the air supply. Leucocytes begin to immigrate into the lumen through the epithelium in such numbers and at such a rate, first mononuclear, and later polymorphonuclear cells, that the epithelium seems to be pushed from its base and forms projecting papillae." These appear macroscopically as "grey translucent nodules". In the final stage large abscesses filled with caseous pus are present; lobes that are not affected become hypertrophied. In the 1940 paper the two authors put on record studies on a large number of laboratory rats of different ages and breed. They showed that animals less than one month old never had lesions and only one out of 14 had the organism in the lungs. 10% of the 1 to 4 month-old rats showed lung lesions and in 36% of them the organism was found. 31% of the 4 to 8 months old animals had lesions and in 65% of these the organism was present. All the very old rats had lesions although the organism was only cultured from 77% of these animals, due mostly to spreading contaminants which rendered the isolation of the PPLO impossible in pre-penicillin times. It is noteworthy that the organism was frequently demonstrated before macroscopical lesions could be discovered. This is what would be expected of an organism which is the aetiological cause of the disease, though microscopical pathological changes were observed in lung sections before macroscopical lesions appeared.

In order to fulfil Koch's third postulate, attempts were made to provoke the outbreak of bronchopneumonia by injections of freshly isolated organisms into very young rats free from disease. All these attempts failed. We had shown that a close relation existed between the presence of the organism and the bronchiectatic lesions, but we could not produce the lesions with the organism. However, in 1954, a discovery of K. K. Cheng came to my assistance. He demonstrated that every young rat developed severe bronchiectasis within one or two weeks after bronchial ligation. Subsequently, it was shown (Klieneberger-Nobel and Cheng, 1955) that after the ligation of a bronchus the PPLO invades the lung and multiplies very rapidly. Two days after the ligation it is present, whereas lesions are not found before the fourth day when the bronchi begin to dilate. After 12 days large abscesses could be found containing pus and innumerable PPLO. Consequently, it was assumed that the PPLO must be latently present in every rat and the factor permitting the invasion of the lungs and the multiplication of the PPLO, followed by the development of the lesions, must be the stagnation of bronchial secretion after the ligation. In order to discover the habitat of the organism in its latent state, I killed a number of weanling rats and searched for PPLO in their lungs and nasopharynx. The lungs were invariably free from PPLO, but a good crop of these organisms was obtained from the nasopharynx. We also examined baby rats delivered by caesarian section, none of which yielded PPLO. We can therefore conclude that the mother rat soon after birth transfers some of her PPLO population to the nasopharynx of her offspring so that every rat thus becomes a carrier of PPLO. Changes in the resistance of the animal brought about by stress, ligation of a bronchus, or age, cause the disease to break out. As the baby rats delivered by caesarian section were free from PPLO it can be hoped that a PPLO-free strain of rats may be developed if these animals are reared by hand. Such projects are being pursued at the present time in some laboratories (see Germ-free vertebrates: present status, 1959).

A serological study of rats with lungs of normal appearance not containing the PPLO, and of rats with lung lesions containing the PPLO, provided additional evidence for the close connection between the presence of the PPLO and the lesions (Lemcke, in the press). A complement fixation test, which will be described in Chapter X, was used for the examination of the rat sera by means of which it was shown that the sera of very young rats (four to eight weeks of age) had little or no antibodies against an antigen prepared from a rat lung strain. On the other hand, the sera of older diseased rats showed antibody titres rising with the degree of bronchiectasis present. It was further shown that the various rat lung strains isolated from different stocks belonged to one serological type, whereas other PPLO isolated from rats with polyarthritis were of a different serological type although these two types do have some common antigen. From our studies of various diseases caused by PPLO it seems that the complement fixation test is highly specific and therefore a reliable serological reaction.

## D.  Misinterpretations of Disease Conditions due to PPLO in Experimental Animals

As seen from the various diseases so far described, pathogenic PPLO have a tendency to remain latent for a time. Only when circumstances arise which lower the host's resistance are they able to multiply and become actively pathogenic with the production of disease. Therefore it is not surprising that in seemingly healthy animals harbouring PPLO a disease due to these organisms flares up when they undergo the stress imposed upon them by experiments. The misinterpretations published in the literature by various workers who were unaware of this fact are of two kinds:

(1) It was concluded that a new virus had been discovered because a disease condition due to experimental injury developed and could be reproduced by a filterable agent. In reality this agent was a PPLO latent in the experimental animal.

(2) PPLO isolated from pathological conditions produced in animals by the application of material from human patients were thought to be of human origin and were interpreted as the cause of human disease of hitherto unknown aetiology. Here also a latent PPLO infection was "lighted up" in the experimental animal. The following examples illustrate the first kind of misinterpretation mentioned above. When Sabin (1938a) transferred a strain of toxoplasma serially by intracerebral inoculation, he found that after a time the mice showed a specific nervous disease in consequence of which they rolled round their longtitudinal axis when placed on a flat surface. This filterable agent could be separated from the toxoplasma and the nervous condition could be passed on from mouse to mouse by intracerebral injections. He believed he had discovered a new virus. In 1933 Findlay had already found that a similar condition which he called "rolling disease" had occurred in mice used for serial intracerebral passages of a strain of yellow fever. In 1937, when passing a strain of lymphocytic choriomeningitis in mice, Findlay found that "rolling disease" had turned up a second time; he also thought that he was dealing with a hitherto unknown virus. He described the pathological lesions produced in rolling disease as follows (Findlay et al. 1938): "Serial sections showed no lesions in the middle ear to account for the rolling symptoms, but there was an intense inflammatory reaction in the brain. This reaction, which was almost entirely a polymorphonuclear leucocytosis with a very few large mononuclear leucocytes, began round the point of insertion of the needle. Polymorphonuclear leucocytes were also seen infiltrating the floor of the lateral ventricles and the choroid plexus, and small masses of polymorphonuclear leucocytes were present in the meninges. In the fully developed condition enormous masses of polymorphonuclear leucocytes were seen forming a lesion which closely resembled an acute abscess." Bacteria could not be grown from the lesions but small granules were discovered in stained smears and therefore Findlay thought the cause of the disease was a virus. Ledingham was of the opinion that a virus was unlikely to produce such a leucocytic infiltra-

tion and suggested to me that I should try to isolate a PPLO and indeed I was able to cultivate on my special media a PPLO (then designated L5) from the brains of all the mice suffering from rolling disease but not from the healthy stock mice. Although Findlay and I were not able to produce rolling disease by intracerebral injection of a broth culture of the organism, the mice promptly developed the disease when we added an agar emulsion as an adjuvant. Sabin, whom we informed of our results, came to similar conclusions (1938b).

A misinterpretation of the same nature is found in an article by Woglom and Warren (1938a, b) who described a "pyogenic filterable agent" in the albino rat. They had been working with a sarcoma of rats which they transferred from animal to animal by subcutaneous injections of tumour emulsions. Although the injected material was bacteriologically sterile, large abscesses developed from time to time; bacteria could not be grown from the pus but the abscesses could be transferred from rat to rat by subcutaneous injection of pus emulsion. I obtained material from such an abscess and cultivated from it a PPLO identical in growth and serological type with the rat polyarthritis strain ("L4") which I had previously isolated from a swollen sub-maxillary gland of a rat (Klieneberger, 1939).

Woglom and Warren's culture was very pathogenic for rats when injected subcutaneously or intraveneously with agar or cells as an adjuvant. When a subcutaneous abscess developed, the organisms were not only found in the pus but also in the heart blood and in the pathologically enlarged spleen. As was shown at a later date (Klieneberger-Nobel, 1960b) the growth of the abscess is always accompanied by a marked production of antibodies in the serum specifically reacting with an "L4" antigen in complement fixation tests. A severe polyarthritis developed when either a culture, together with an adjuvant, or an emulsion of pus, were injected intraveneously. Rats which recovered from the polyarthritis or from the subcutaneous abscesses were immune to new injections of "L4". Beeuwkes and Collier (1942), who studied the infective rat polyarthritis years before the discovery of its cause, confirmed my findings later on, as did Woglom and Warren (1939).

The second type of misinterpretation is illustrated by the following: when Swift and Brown (1939) inoculated mice intranasally with arthritic and pleural exudates from patients suffering from acute rheumatic fever, they obtained pneumonic lesions and subsequently were able to culture a PPLO from the mouse lung. They also induced lesions on chorioallantoic membranes of chicken embryos with similar exudates. Although they reserved their final judgement they thought they might have discovered the cause of rheumatic fever. However, all they had done was to light up a latent PPLO infection in the mice, for it has been shown by various authors (Sullivan and Dienes, 1939;

Edward, 1940, 1947a) that intranasal inoculation of mice with lung suspension of another mouse can produce pneumonic lesions. From these lesions a PPLO can be grown in pure culture. The pneumonic conditions can be transferred in serial passages by nasal instillation of diseased mouse lung suspension. As Edward had shown, mice may harbour the special PPLO in their noses and it has been demonstrated that by nasal instillation under ether narcosis of various irritating materials, such as diphtheria toxin or cell suspensions of lung or brain, this organism can be induced to settle and multiply in the lungs and cause pneumonia.

Sullivan and Dienes (1939) described the disease as follows: "When a large number of mice were simultaneously inoculated with a suspension of the same infective material*, it was observed that during the first day there was little change in their clinical appearance except for slight ruffling of the fur. However, even by the end of the first 24 hours, there were small 1-2 mm. purple consolidated areas close to the hilar great vessels. Sickness progressed rapidly, with failure to eat or drink, and loss of weight. Some became markedly dyspnoeic. These began to die about the third day, and exhibited almost total pulmonary consolidation. Microscopically the pneumonia was largely interstitial, with mononuclear phagocytes the dominant cells. Some of these were in mitosis, others actively phagocytic, and a few by fusion formed large giant cells. The consolidated areas were congested. Polymorphonuclear leucocytes were present and especially numerous within the small bronchi. There were a few areas of compensatory alveolar emphysema."

Further examples of erroneous interpretations of experiments in small laboratory animals and in chick embryos may be found in the following papers (Grünholz, 1950; Shepard, 1956, 1958, see also Klieneberger-Nobel, 1960b). The examples mentioned above demonstrate the dangers involved when experimenting with living entities harbouring latent PPLO.

## E. Various PPLO Discovered at a Later Period

The isolation of PPLO from dogs, first described by Shoetensack, was again reported by Edward and Fitzgerald in 1951a. They found by serological and cultural methods that most of the strains which they had isolated from the vagina and the throat could be classified into three groups, provisionally designated by them as α, β and γ. It is noteworthy that all the α strains were derived from the vagina. About $\frac{2}{3}$ of the β strains came from the throat, $\frac{1}{3}$ from the vagina and the γ strains

---

* Pneumonic lung suspension.

were also less frequently isolated from the vagina than from the throat. It has been suggested (Chu and Beveridge, 1954) that PPLO may have a certain pathogenicity for dogs in causing inflammation and purulent discharge of the genital organs. If so, the α strains should be suspected in the first place, although convincing evidence of their harmfulness for dogs has so far not been forthcoming.

In cattle, PPLO not identical with the organism of pleuropneumonia bovis have also been found on the genital organs (Edward *et al.* 1947). Edward (1950a) reports on two members of the group, provisionally called the P and S species, which he isolated from this site. The S strains show cultural and serological similarities to the previously mentioned saprophytic strains of Laidlaw and Elford and of Seiffert. The P strains are more exacting than the S strains in their cultural requirements. There is a suggestion that the P strains may cause inflammatory changes in the genital tract predisposing to infertility and that they are possibly pathogens (Edward, 1952).

Some diseases of cattle (Carter, 1954) and goats (Cordy *et al.* 1955) from which PPLO of uncertain nature were isolated, have been described in the literature. The authors have given detailed reports of the conditions in the animals but they have not satisfactorily compared their newly isolated strains with cultures of known origin or type. It seems desirable that a reference laboratory able to diagnose strains should be set up in order to determine the type of strain isolated in outbreaks of disease of unknown aetiology.

The PPLO frequently isolated from poultry and turkeys are not discussed here as their significance in relation to disease in these birds seems to be doubtful. The coccobacilliform bodies, however, which seem to be pathogenic for domestic birds, will be dealt with in Chapter VI.

## F. PPLO Occurring in Man

In 1937, Dienes and Edsall cultured PPLO for the first time from a Bartholin's gland; a dense growth of the organism unaccompanied by bacterial growth was obtained. This finding aroused great interest and many workers showed subsequently that PPLO occur frequently on the genitals of both sexes. They are thought by some authors to cause venereal disease and in particular non-gonococcal urethritis in males (Harkness, 1950); however, they also occur in people without symptoms as well as in the diseased. The resulting controversies will be discussed in Chapter X in which I propose to deal with the pathogenicity of PPLO; much of the literature concerned may be found in the reviews by Edward (1954), Klieneberger-Nobel (1954), Freundt (1958), Köhler (1960) and in the paper by Dienes *et al.* (1948). Here I shall report only on the various types of organisms in man and their habitat.

It seems that there is mainly one species which occurs on human genitals. Nicol and Edward (1953) found that out of 91 strains isolated from human genitals, 90 belong to one and the same serological type which I shall call in the following "the human genital type" (*Mycoplasma hominis*, Edward and Freundt, 1956). In my laboratory well over 100 genital PPLO strains have been isolated of which about 70 have been tested serologically. All these have been shown to belong to the human genital type.

A strain isolated several times by Ruiter and Wentholt (1950, 1952, 1953a, b, 1955) from the genital mucosa in gangrenous lesions with a fusospirillary flora, was designated "G type" by them. The colonies of the G strains are fairly large with a small but pronounced centre. They are obligate anaerobes unlike the human genital organisms that grow equally well aerobically and anaerobically. Swelling of joints and abscesses can be produced in young white mice by injection of these organisms when they are first isolated.

The isolation of PPLO from human throats and specimens of saliva was first reported by Smith and Morton (1951a) and Morton *et al.* (1951). Dienes and Madoff (1953) obtained PPLO from teeth scrapings and from material expressed from the crypts of the tonsils. When Card (1959) examined teeth scrapings in my laboratory she found that the oral PPLO strains are almost ubiquitous. These strains differ from the human genital strains in appearance; their colonies are usually smooth whereas those of the genital strains show some structure. Furthermore, our oral strains grow well anaerobically but hardly at all under aerobic conditions, and have some antigen in common with the human genital strains, although in cross complement fixation tests, Card (1959) has shown that they are serologically distinct and represent a type of their own. As they are so widespread they can be regarded as saprophytes.

Huijsmans-Evers and Ruys (1956a, b) isolated a number of strains from human genitals and showed by means of cultural, biochemical and serological tests (complement fixation) that they could be divided into three groups : (1) the human genital type which they call *Mycoplasma hominis**, (2) the oral type which they call *Mycoplasma salivarium** and the G type (Ruiter and Wentholt) which they call *Mycoplasma fermentans* because it fermented glucose and some other carbohydrates in their tests. Thus it can be seen that they found the same types as the other workers mentioned above, with the exception of two strains which did not react with any of their immune sera and furthermore grew on media which were not enriched with normal serum. They behaved in this respect similarly to the saprophytic strains obtained by Laidlaw and Elford from sewage.

* According to Edward and Freundt (1956).

A few strains which differ from the three types mentioned have apparently been isolated in America (see Nicol and Edward, 1953). It can therefore be concluded that three main types of PPLO occur in man, but additional odd organisms have been reported. Should any of the organisms isolated be responsible for such a common condition as non-gonococcal urethritis, as has been suggested, it must be a type occurring frequently. In order to be able to draw any conclusions it seems of paramount importance that strains isolated should be typed. So far the most reliable method for this typing is the complement fixation reaction*. What applies to the human strains also applies to strains cultivated from animals because experience has shown that in animals suffering from PPLO disease several types of PPLO occur, only one of which can be regarded as the aetiological cause of the condition concerned.

* Villemot and Provost (1959a, b, c, 1960) and Provost and Villemot (1959) have tried to type a number of strains by different serological methods. However, their results seem to be in disagreement with those of other workers who carried out serological tests. Their results have therefore to await confirmation.

# CHAPTER III

# Morphology of Pleuropneumonia-like Organisms

It is difficult from a study of the literature to vizualize what PPLO are really like. We often read that "rings", "filaments" and other "bizarre forms" occur besides small "elementary bodies" or granules. Such a description is misleading and implies that the growth of these organisms is built up of a number of elements of various shapes, just as many fragments combine to give a kaleidoscopic picture. Yet this is not so. If we want to understand the peculiar but simple morphology of these organisms we must first form a clear concept of their nature. It has been shown during the last few years that they have no rigid cell walls and no cell wall substances (Kandler and Zehender, 1957), properties which distinguish them from bacteria and all other microbes. It should further be realized that their cytoplasm is more difficult to stain than that of other microorganisms and this applies particularly to their young stages. Their growth and individual particles are very soft, frag-ile and easily destroyed, and they do not withstand the common bacteriological methods of preparation, fixation and staining of smears. Moreover, their shapes and sizes are more variable than those of other microbes and dependent on their accidental environment. Special methods have been devised for their study under various con-ditions of growth; such methods should all be used comparatively and then by a process of abstraction a picture of their real likeness and development will gradually be obtained. I would like to outline my own idea of their developmental pattern and then describe the various methods for their demonstration and the results so produced.

## A. Outline of Development

Whether growing in liquid or on solid media the organism goes re-peatedly through a cycle of morphological changes. The smallest unit is a granule (minimal reproductive unit), spherical, with a diameter of about 125 m$\mu$ which does not multiply as such but grows into a soft particle of protoplasm without a rigid cell wall, hereafter called "the PPLO-cell". This PPLO-cell can assume various shapes and divide by segmentation into a number of similar PPLO-cells which eventually produce granules (minimal reproductive units). Prior to this develop-ment a differentiation of the cytoplasm into concentrated and thinner areas takes place and the granules arise from the concentrated material. The number of regularly distributed granules arising in each PPLO-cell is directly proportional to its size.

## 1. *Growth on Solid Media*

The granule (minimal reproductive unit) (Fig. 4, (1)) grows into a soft, droplet-like PPLO-cell (Fig. 4, (2)a) which in its further development is influenced by its environment. The granules spread out on the solid medium into flat, disk-like or irregularly shaped PPLO-cells such as those depicted in Fig. 4, (2) b and c, which divide by segmentation until a small colony has been produced. The very flat PPLO-cells are, on the solid medium, often of a considerable size, particularly at the periphery and on top of the colonies. However, in the centre of the colonies the PPLO-cells are usually drawn down into the medium and here small forms are mainly produced, a process accounting for the characteristic appearance of the colonies. It should be emphasized here that small and large PPLO-cells are potentially similar and differ only in dimensions. As development progresses differentiation takes place in the material making up the PPLO-cells and consequently both concentrated and thin areas arise within each element and ridges of very solid cytoplasm appear around the whole, or part, of the circumference (Fig. 4 (3)). The concentrated material divides within the PPLO-cells and thus produces the granules (minimal reproductive units) (Fig. 4, (4)). Only one layer of granules develops and this lies in the same plane owing to the shallowness of the mother PPLO-cell. The granules are frequently very regularly arranged and form a dense chain around the circumference of the mother PPLO-cell. This characteristic appearance is an exclusive feature of PPLO-cells which have developed minimal reproductive units. The newly formed granules grow again into a new generation of larger elements as long as enough nutrients are available (Fig. 4, (5)); thus larger and larger colonies may develop.

## 2. *Growth in Liquid Media*

The small granule (minimal reproductive unit, Fig. 5, (1)) develops into a small globular, disk-like, pleomorphic or filamentous PPLO-cell (Fig. 5 (2)). Whereas the minimal reproductive units have a diameter of approximately 125 mμ, the bigger PPLO-cells into which they grow in the liquid medium have a size of about 300 mμ. It must be attributed to the molecular forces of the liquid phase acting on the plastic growing PPLO-cells that their shapes and sizes differ in the liquid from those on solid medium; however, intrinsically they do not differ and follow the same trend of development. In the liquid medium, as on the solid, a change takes place within the PPLO-cells after the first period of growth and division and a concentration of matter occurs in some places with the development of dense ridges at the periphery of the globular, disk-like and pleomorphic PPLO-cells (Fig. 5, (3)).

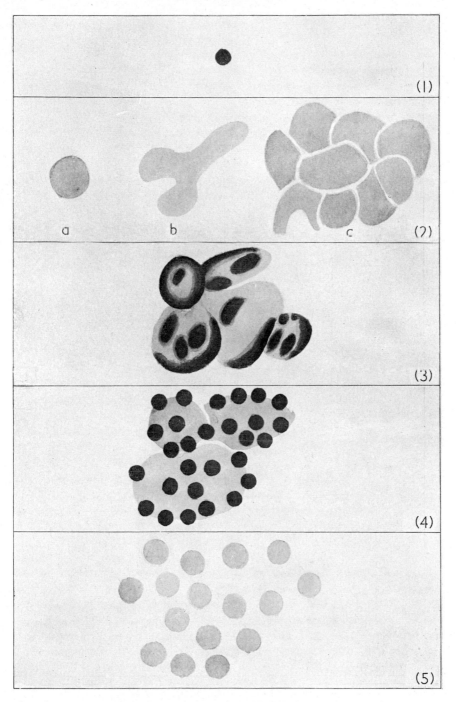

Fig. 4.  Diagram of development of organisms of the pleuropneumonia group on solid medium. (Drawn by Anastasia Theofanides).

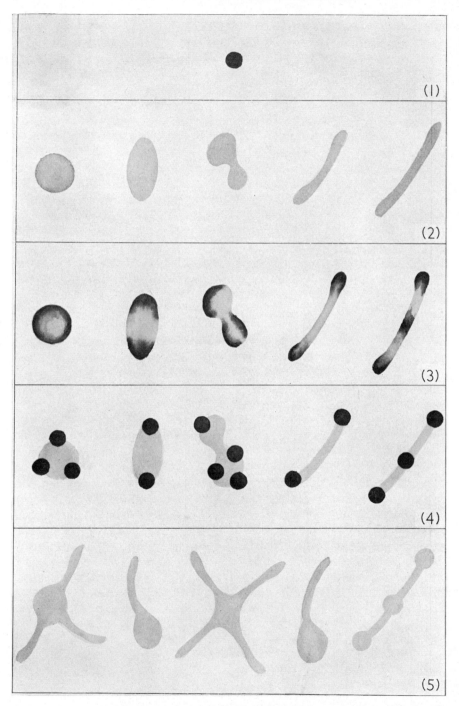

FIG. 5.　Diagram of development of organisms of the pleuropneumonia group in liquid medium. (Drawn by Anastasia Theofanides).

In the case of short filaments these concentrations develop at the poles only. However, in the long filaments they may be evenly distributed along their whole length and it is the concentrated material that again produces the minimal reproductive units. If the filaments are long they produce rows of granules; if they are short, only two granules are formed, one on either end, whereas in the pleomorphic PPLO-cells the granules are arranged peripherally. (Fig. 5, (4)). A single PPLO-cell may produce one, two or more granules, according to its size, in the same way as on the solid medium, and the granules grow out again as long as sufficient nutrient is available and a new development of PPLO-cells takes place. As the granules may either be shed or may remain attached to the mother PPLO-cell all kinds of configurations can arise by the outgrowth of the granules as diagramatically shown in Fig. 5, (5). The famous aster form, from which the name "asterococcus" for the organism of pleuropneumonia bovis was derived, can thus be explained and the production of long, branched filaments consisting of granules or small bodies still connected by cytoplasmic strands which, however, soon disintegrate, can easily be understood.

Although the appearance of the growth seems to be different on solid and in liquid media, development follows the same pattern. The "pleomorphism" which has given rise to so much controversy in the literature through differences of interpretation is nothing else but *thema cum variationes*; the emphasis should be on the development of the organism rather than on its individual forms. This will become even clearer when the various images obtained by different methods of demonstration are discussed in a later paragraph.

## B.  Methods for the Demonstration of PPLO

### 1. *Demonstration of Growth on Solid Media*

The appearances of growth on solid media are fairly uniform as long as low magnification is used; the various species of the group have a similar colony structure which is best seen at magnifications varying between 1 : 30 and 1 : 100 (Figs. 6, 7, 8, 9). However, when high power, and particularly when oil immersion objectives are used to resolve the elements of growth, the difficulties begin because it is not possible due to their softness to see the elements distinctly in a stained smear or in a loopful of material rubbed into a drop of water and covered with a coverslip; special methods of preparation have, therefore, to be used.

### (a) *Direct Agar Microscopy*

A simple way of obtaining at least a picture of the general arrangement of the growth is to cut out a piece of agar from a plate showing

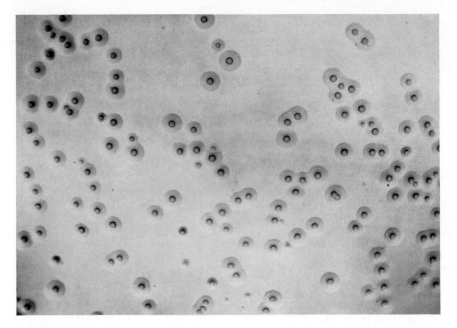

FIG. 6.   Colonies of 4 day old culture of "G" strain (Ruiter and Wentholt, 1953) on solid medium, smooth type of colony. Magnification: × 40. (From thesis of H. M. Wentholt, Groningen, 1952).

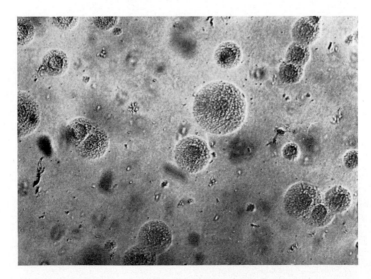

FIG. 7.   Colonies of human genital PPLO strain grown for 2 days on solid medium, smooth type of colony. Magnification: × 100.

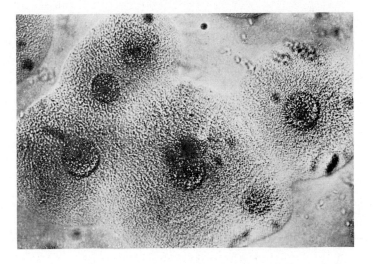

FIG. 8.   Colonies of organism of pleuropneumonia of goats, grown for two days on
solid medium, smooth type of colony. Magnification: × 100.

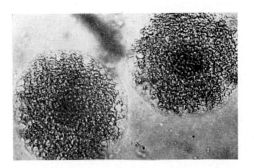

FIG. 9.   Colonies of human genital PPLO strain grown for 3 days on solid medium,
coarse type. Magnification: × 100.

the desired growth and to lower as cautiously as possible the inoculated
side carrying the colonies onto a coverslip. The piece of agar, with
growth and coverslip on top, can now be placed on a slide and sealed
to it with paraffin wax so that the preparation can be inspected by
light field or phase contrast microscopy with the help of a long distance
condenser. By this method single elements can be detected, although
the structure of the delicate elements can neither be resolved, nor the

development of the growth be followed with advantage. In order to do this the contrast of the preparation has to be increased and it can be done by the following method.

## (b)  *Annular Oblique Incident Illumination*

In the work carried out by the author with J. Smiles (1942) annular oblique incident illumination was used. The illuminator was an "Ultro-pak" designed by Leitz to work with an objective having a numerical aperture of 1·0 and an initial magnification of ×75. "Parallel-faced metal rings (external diameter 1·6 cm.) are dipped into hot wax and sealed to a sterile microscope slide, thus forming a small dish the depth of which may be conveniently taken as 0·2 cm; the medium is poured into this dish from a pipette until the surface is slightly above the level of the ring. When it has set, a small loopful of inoculum is placed on the exposed surface of the medium on which a round coverslip is well pressed down by means of a hot metal ring until it comes into contact with the waxed ring which at the same time seals the cover to the micro-dish." In order to absorb light scattered by the medium, a black dye, naphthalene blue black (1/2000 dilution) was introduced into the medium. This had no inhibitory effect on the growth and a true dark-ground picture was obtained with details of structure that ordinary darkground cannot provide.

## (c)  *A Darkfield Illumination Method applied to Growth on Solid Medium*

A method which uses ordinary darkfield illumination and shows the organisms as they have grown on solid medium has recently been devised by the author. It gives fairly good resolution and is simple to carry out. This procedure has proved to be useful for other purposes also and I will refer to it again later. It uses a "Formvar*" film over-laying a piece of agar which is produced in the following way: Square pieces, slightly smaller than the coverslips to be used, are cut out of a nutrient agar plate and placed on sterile slides. A solution of 0·3% "Formvar" in pure chloroform is quickly poured over the agar pieces and allowed to drain off by tilting the slide, thus producing a fine film on the agar after the evaporation of the chloroform. The slides are now placed in sterile Petri dishes and, with a finely drawn out capil-lary pipette, small droplets of a dilution of organisms in Tyrode-

* Formvar, grade 1595 E from Shawinigan Ltd., Marlow House, Lloyds Avenue, London, E.C.3.

Ringer* or phosphate buffer solution in high quality deionized water
are placed on the membranes. The cultures are incubated in a moist
chamber as long as desired. By altering the dilution of the inoculum
and the periods of incubation, various developmental stages of the
organisms are obtained. When the desired growth has developed the
membranes are floated on Tyrode-Ringer solution, then caught on a
slide and covered with a coverslip. Excess liquid is pressed out between
layers of filter paper and the preparation may be sealed at the edges
with paraffin wax to prevent evaporation. It will be found that some
of the elements have floated off the membrane and show Brownian
movement; however, in other places the growth is still fixed to the
membrane in its original arrangement so that it can be studied by
darkfield illumination and photographed.

## (d)  Staining Method of Dienes (1939, 1942, 1945)

A mixture of an alcoholic solution of methylene blue and azure II
is used for staining without previous fixation†. A droplet of this mixture is spread on a coverslip and allowed to dry. An agar piece carrying the growth is cut out and its growth-bearing surface placed on the
prepared coverslip at the same time avoiding any sliding movement.
The agar background remains unstained but the PPLO colonies stain
quite intensely and can be studied at various magnifications. If the
agar piece is too thick a thin slice carrying the growth can be cut off
with a razor blade and transferred to the coverslip. Sealing with paraffin wax may keep the preparation for a few days; alternatively, the
stained agar section on the coverslip can be left to dry in the air and
then be taken into xylene and from this into Canada balsam. The
method can be recommended for the quick identification of PPLO as
it shows the characteristic of the growth as well as the single elements
satisfactorily, yet when it is desired to see detail of structure of
the various elements the present author prefers the two following
methods.

## (e)  Agar Fixation Method of Klieneberger (Klieneberger and Smiles, 1942; Klieneberger-Nobel, 1950, 1954)

This method can be used to fix and stain colonies that have already
developed. Pieces of agar carrying the growth are cut out and lowered

* Sodium chloride 0.2 g.; potassium chloride 0.2 g.; calcium chloride 0.2 g.; glucose
1.0 g.; sodium phosphate (Na H$_2$ PO$_4$) 0.05 g.; sodium bicarbonate 1.0 g.; deionized
water 1 litre; all substances of analytical grade.
† Methylene blue 0.5 g.; Azure II 0.25 g.; Maltose 2.0 g.; Na$_2$CO$_3$ 0.05 g.; benzoic
acid 0.04 g.; dist. water 20.0 ml.; dissolve and filter before use.

face down on coverslips which, with adhering agar pieces on top, are placed in watch glasses and covered with Bouin's solution*. The best results, however, are obtained when the agar pieces are cut out of the plate directly after inoculation and placed on coverslips on which they are incubated in a moist chamber so that the growth develops between the agar piece and the glass surface. After the desired period of incubation the preparations are ready for fixation which takes place by diffusion through the agar. Fixation is complete after about 8 hours but can conveniently take place overnight without adverse effect. The agar blocks are then peeled off the coverslips which are then washed in water until the yellowness of the picric acid has disappeared. The coverslips are stained in Giemsa solution diluted 1 in 50 with a mixture of equal parts of London tap water and distilled water or a phosphate buffer solution (pH 6·8) and they remain in the stain for 8 to 24 hours according to the stages present in the culture and the effect desired. A good idea of the progress of the staining is obtained by floating the coverslip on a slide and by looking at it with a high dry lens. When found to be sufficiently stained the preparation is dehydrated. At first the stain is cautiously removed with filter paper, but before the coverslip is completely dry it is passed through the following acetone-xylene mixtures: (i) acetone 19 ml. xylene 1 ml. (ii) acetone 14 ml. xylene 6 ml. (iii) acetone 6 ml. xylene 14 ml. (iv) two or three changes of xylene. Finally the preparation is mounted in Canada balsam. The transfer from one mixture into the next must proceed as quickly as possible, but allowing enough time for the elimination of the water. This method produces good pictures of colonies, and the centres as well as the peripheral zones adhere to the coverslip. The fine-structure of the elements is particularly well brought out in the thinnest parts of the preparations. The finest detail of delicate growth that can be seen in a stained preparation is, however, best demonstrated by the following method.

## (f) *Fixing and Staining of Growth on a "Formvar" Film*

Cultures on membranes are prepared as described under (c). When the desired growth has taken place they are floated on Tyrode-Ringer or phosphate buffer solution containing 10% formaldehyde (the percentage does not seem to be of importance). After three minutes fixation they are floated on distilled water for washing and left 15 to 30 minutes. They are then lifted out on a coverslip, dried, stained, dehydrated and mounted as described under (e). This is the best method for the light microscopical demonstration of the structure of the ele-

---

* Picric acid: sat. aq. sol. 75 ml; formalin 25 ml.; glacial acetic acid 5 ml.

ments, their delicacy and arrangement. Its further advantage is that the growth is not disturbed by preparation, for all the growth that develops is lying on top of the membrane, since the elements cannot penetrate the membrane except through holes. In sufficiently thin areas very good resolution of the elements is obtained. However, electron micrographs have given us (Klieneberger-Nobel and Cuckow, 1955; Cuckow and Klieneberger-Nobel, 1955) an even better understanding of the organisation and development of PPLO and have confirmed what the other methods taught us previously.

### (g) *Electron Micrographs of Growth on Solid Media*

The method described above is used here. After fixing and washing, the Formvar membranes are placed on copper grids in such a way that the grids are covered by an area containing growth. The preparations are then dried and shadowed and micrographs are produced as reported in the afore-mentioned papers.

### 2. *Demonstration of Growth in Liquid Media*

### (a) *Darkground Illumination Method*

This method has been used widely in the past and can still be informative if the necessary precautions are taken. In order to obtain a good scattering of light and an easily visible suspension it is usually advisable to spin the culture down and to resuspend the sediment in a small amount of medium. Slides and coverslips have to be scrupulously clean which can be effected by pulling them through the flame 10 to 20 times in quick succession after cleaning them in the ordinary way. Of course, both slides and coverslips have to be of the correct thickness for the optical system. A droplet of the suspension is placed on the slide which is then inverted and slowly lowered down on to a fairly large coverslip. The excess fluid is pressed out between layers of filter paper to produce a very thin layer of liquid; the edges of the coverslip are sealed with paraffin wax. It is advisable to carry out examinations of the culture under investigation at various ages in order to obtain the fullest information. The easiest organisms to examine by this method are those of bovine and caprine pleuropneumonia and agalactia.

### (b) *Stained Preparations*

A drop from a broth culture which has been dried, fixed and stained, can hardly be expected to give information in so soft an organism. Yet it is possible to obtain good preparations if the following method is adopted. Drops of freshly inoculated broth are placed on sterile cover-slips and are covered with blocks of semi-solid agar medium and in-cubated in a moist chamber. The agar fixation method as described under 1 (e) can then be applied.

## (c) *Electron Micrographs of Growth in Liquid Media*

By far the best method for the demonstration of growth from liquid medium is provided by electron microscopy. We prepared our speci-mens as follows: a culture in liquid medium was spun down and the pellet resuspended in Tyrode-Ringer solution 3 to 4 times (or more) the volume of the original medium. A Formvar membrane produced on a slide from a 0·3% solution in pure chloroform was floated on 10% formaldehyde in either Tyrode-Ringer solution or water and droplets of the PPLO suspension were placed on its surface and left for three minutes to fix by diffusion through the membrane. The membranes were refloated on distilled water and washed for 30 minutes, where-upon the rest of the procedure was carried out according to 1(g).

## 3. *Demonstration of PPLO in Pathological Samples*

Illustrations are found in the literature which are supposed to demonstrate PPLO in pathological samples. Some of these show non-descript small particles apparently inside (or on top of?) the cytoplasm of cells; unfortunately, it is not possible to distinguish these particles from cellular debris or remnants of bacteria. However, when an abundance of the organism is present in an exudate it is sometimes possible to show large clusters of organisms in such a simple preparation as a smear fixed with methyl alcohol and stained with Giemsa solution. The only foolproof method for their demonstration is still actual cultivation from pathological specimens. On the other hand, one method which the author has often applied to material from infected animals is worth trying and may give a quicker result than culture, which nevertheless must always be carried out for true identification.

A drop of the exudate is spread on a Formvar film overlying a slice of medium and after 0, 5 and 8 hours the films are fixed and stained as described under 1 (f). Good pictures of the first growth after 5 and 8 hours of incubation can thus be obtained and an opinion can be formed as to whether multiplication of the elements has taken place. An early diagnosis is then possible and the mistaking of unrelated par-ticulate matter for elements of growth can be excluded. The success of this method depends upon the number of PPLO in the original sample. The final proof of the presence of PPLO must therefore always be a culture of characteristic appearance which can be serially subcultured.

## C. Images Obtained by Various Methods

### 1. *From Solid Media*

The images obtained by the various methods are best explained with the help of illustrations. In Figs. 6, 7, 8, 9 colonies of various PPLO are seen at low magnifications. Figure 6 shows colonies of Ruiter and Wentholt's human "G strain" which had grown for 4 days on solid medium. These colonies show characteristic dark centres and trans-

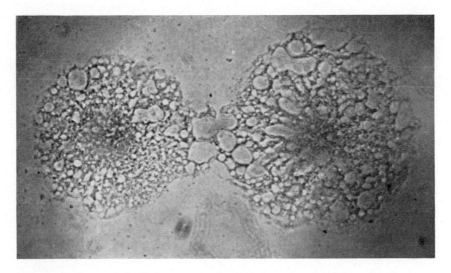

Fig. 10. Two colonies of a human genital PPLO strain of coarse type, phase contrast method. Magnification: × 200.

parent peripheral zones but no surface structures. Figure 7 depicts the colonies of a human genital strain grown for two days; they have a granular appearance. The colonies shown in Fig. 6 (× 40) and Fig. 7 (× 100) measure 50 to 150μ in diameter. Those of Fig. 8 (colonies of the organism of pleuropneumonia of goats, × 100) are very granular in appearance, although all these colonies could be called "smooth" in comparison with those shown in Fig. 9 which are from a human genital strain of coarse appearance. The dark central zone is surrounded by a peripheral zone of lace-like structure. Granular or smooth growth is sometimes characteristic for a certain species but it is often found that one and the same strain can produce both types of colonies.

Figure 10 shows coarse colonies similar to Fig. 9 but viewed under phase contrast illumination with a better resolution and at a slightly higher magnification ($\times$ 200). The superficial impression of this image is that of crochet work consisting of holes and more solid surroundings. However, if the picture is perused closely it can be seen that there is very delicate matter within some of the "holes", and the "solid sur-

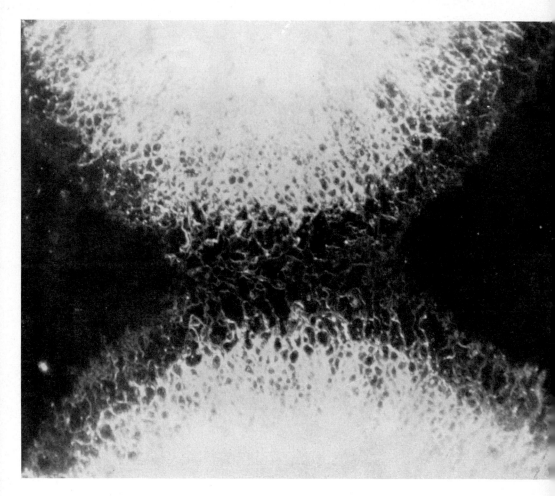

FIG. 11. Organism of bovine pleuropneumonia, 4 day old confluent growth between two colonies on solid medium, "Ultropak" dark field method. Magnification: $\times$ 1200. (First published by Klieneberger and Smiles, 1942).

rounding zone" is interspersed with granules and little bodies. In reality the whole surface of the colony is composed of flat PPLO-cells, very thin in the middle, with more condensed material round the periphery where granules and new little cells have been produced.

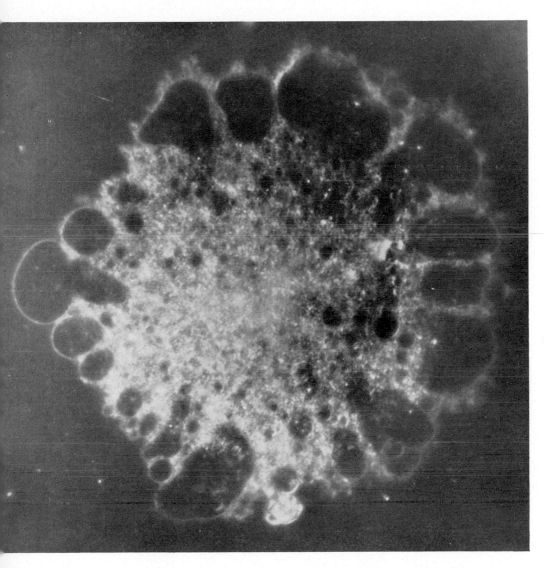

FIG. 12. Asterococcus canis Shoetensack, 2 day old colony on solid medium, "Ultropak" dark field method. Magnification: × 1200. (First published by Klieneberger and Smiles 1942).

The accompanying two illustrations, Figs. 11 and 12, photographed at high magnifications by the "Ultropak" method, demonstrate the structure of a surface colony even better. Figure 11 shows sectors of two colonies of the organism of bovine pleuropneumonia the peripheral

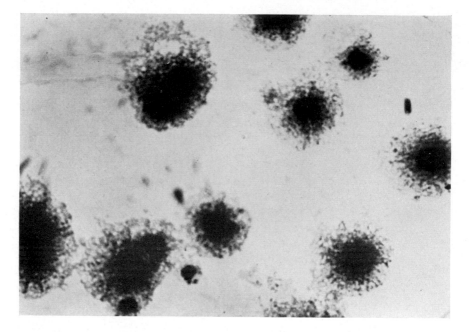

FIG. 13. Colonies of a human genital PPLO strain (grown for 4 days on solid medium) as they appear after agar-fixation-Giemsa treatment at a magnification: × 100. Colonies well isolated and large.

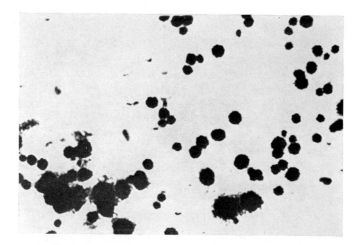

FIG. 14. Colonies of a human genital PPLO strain (grown for 4 days on solid medium) as they appear after agar-fixation-Giemsa treatment at a magnification: × 100. Colonies densely grown and small, consisting almost entirely of central part.

zones of which have joined up. These are composed of pleomorphic PPLO-cells so thin that they appear empty; they show granules and little bodies within their more condensed edges. Figure 12 shows a similar colony this time of Shoetensack's *Asterococcus canis* with a border

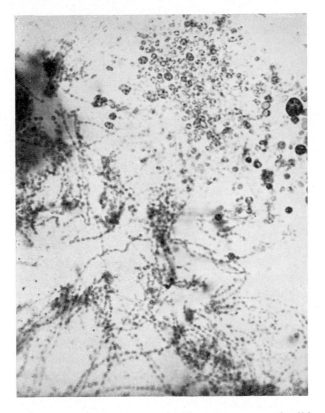

Fig. 15. Organism of bovine pleuropneumonia grown on semi-solid medium for two days. Agar fixation-Giemsa method. Magnification: × 1800. Note the granules in some of the PPLO cells in the top-most part of the picture.

of very large apparently empty PPLO-cells each surrounded by little granules and globules.

Figures 13 and 14 show colonies of a human genital strain as they appear under low magnification after agar fixation and Giemsa staining. The illustrations show that the colonies both large (Fig. 13) and small (Fig. 14), adhere *in toto* to the coverslip after application of this method. Figure 15 represents growth of the organism of bovine pleuropneumonia from semi-solid medium (agar fixation-Giemsa method) seen at high magnification. At the bottom of the picture are seen strings of tiny globules, a typical growth form of this organism in liquid and

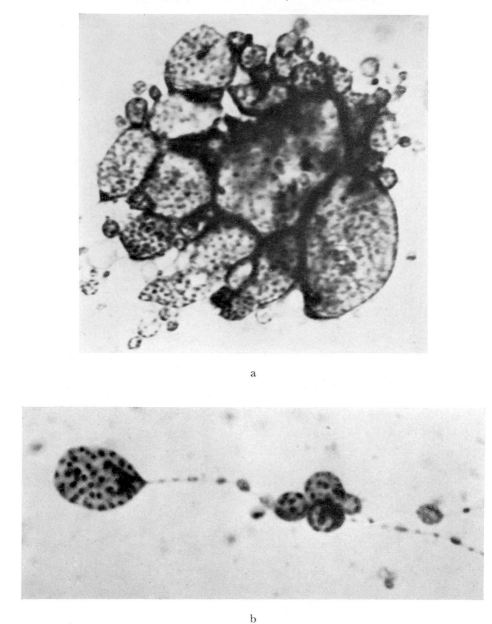

a

b

FIGS. 16a and 16b.  PPLO from the rat lung grown on solid medium for 3 days.
Agar fixation-Giemsa method. Magnification:  × 2000.
Note the regularly arranged minimal reproductive units all lying in the same focal
plane of the thin but extended mother cells.

on wet solid medium. It can be assumed that here this filamentous form of growth developed in a little pool of liquid on top of the semi-solid medium. The upper right part of the same photograph shows the typical appearance of growth on a semi-solid surface. Here small disks have developed which show an assortment of granules growing into new PPLO-cells. Figure 16a illustrates growth of a rat lung organism (agar fixation-Giemsa technique) which produced a small colony on solid medium. The PPLO-cells are filled with granules, all lying in the

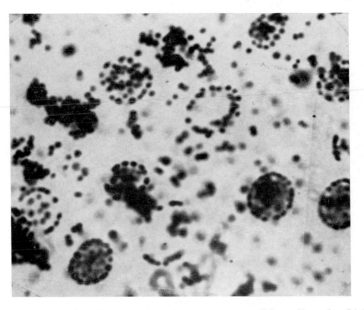

Fig. 17. Sewage organism, "Laidlaw A", grown on solid medium for 24 hours. Formvar film-Giemsa method. Magnification: × 3000. Note the minimal reproductive units which have started to grow again.

same focal plane owing to the thinness of the cells. Figure 16b shows a single cell of the same organism attached to a delicate filament.

In Fig. 17 a picture is seen of Laidlaw and Elford's sewage organism which had developed on a Formvar film overlying nutrient agar and was subsequently fixed and stained after 24 hours of incubation. In place of the original disks, new granules can be seen which have started a new generation of PPLO-cells, while their position still indicates the outline of the mother PPLO-cell. A particularly dense peripheral circle of granules can be recognized in the place where the mother disks previously carried concentrated ridges of cytoplasm.

The three following illustrations (Figs. 18, 19, 20) are photographs of the organism of agalactia grown on Formvar films overlying nutrient agar. Most of the delicate PPLO-cells, whether large or small, show

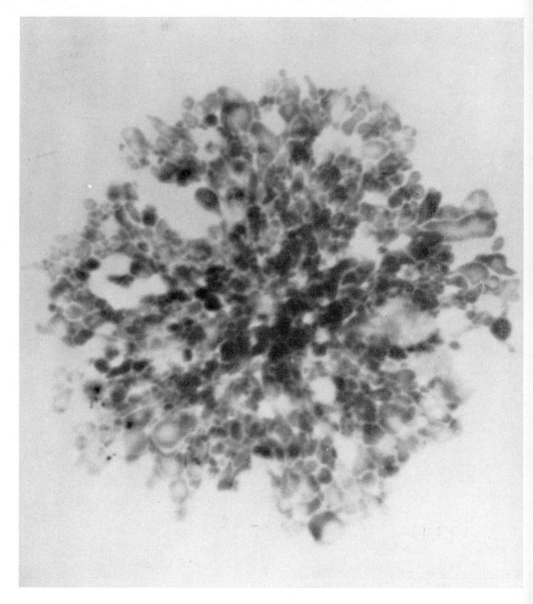

FIG. 18.  Microcolony of the organism of agalactia of sheep and goats grown on solid medium overnight. Formvar film-Giemsa method. Magnification: × 3200. Note the large but delicate PPLO-cells with their more concentrated ridges. (First published by Klieneberger-Nobel, 1956).

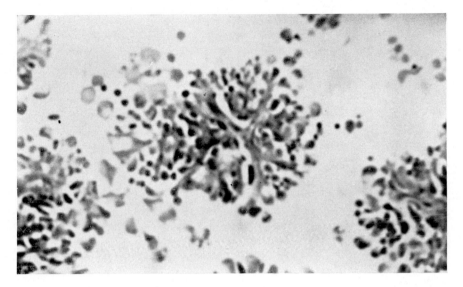

FIG. 19.  Organism of agalactia of sheep and goats grown on solid medium over-
night. Formvar film-Giemsa method. Magnification: × 2000. Note the differentiation into lighter and darker parts.

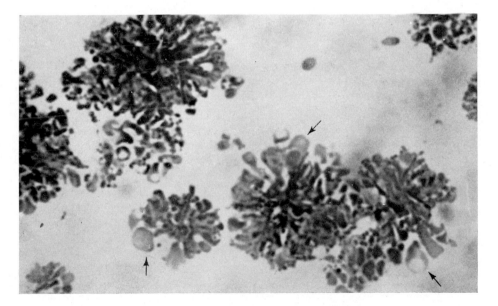

FIG. 20.  Organism of agalactia of sheep and goats grown on solid medium over-
night. Formvar film-Giemsa method. Magnification: × 2000. Note the peripheral
ridges.

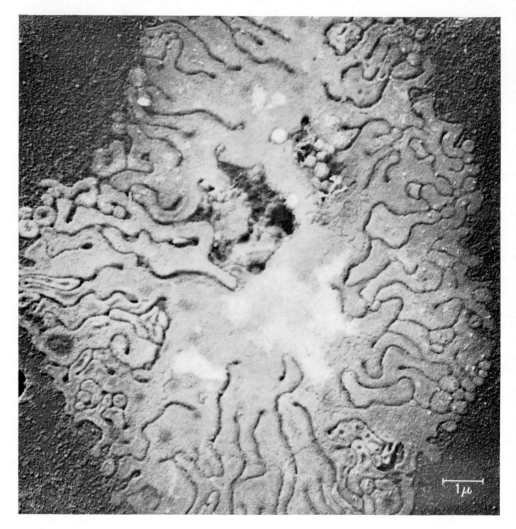

Fig. 21. Electron micrograph of a young microcolony of a human genital PPLO shadowed with gold–palladium alloy at an angle of approximately 30°, taken with a Philips electron microscope with an electron beam of 60 k.v.

concentrations of matter around their peripheries and are probably in the stage preceding granule formation.

The best concept of the nature of PPLO can be gained from electron micrographs. Figure 21 shows a young colony of a human genital PPLO which gives an excellent impression of the softness of the living material as it "flowed" over the surface of the medium while growing, thereby producing at the periphery numerous filamentous strands in

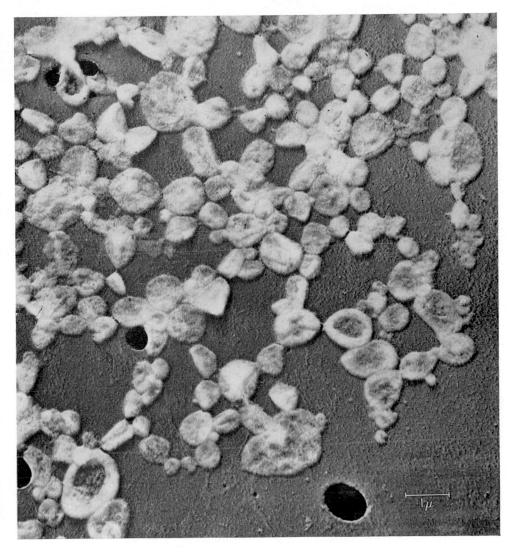

FIG. 22. Electron micrograph of the organism of agalactia of sheep and goats shadowed and taken as 21. Note the cells with thin and concentrated parts.

the process of dividing and branching. This specimen was shadowed with gold-palladium alloy at an angle of approximately 30°C and the low shadows show better than anything else the thinness of the PPLO-cells. Some of the peripheral elements have differentiated into a thinner central part and a more concentrated outer part. Figure 22 illustrates, in a slightly more advanced growth stage, the organism of

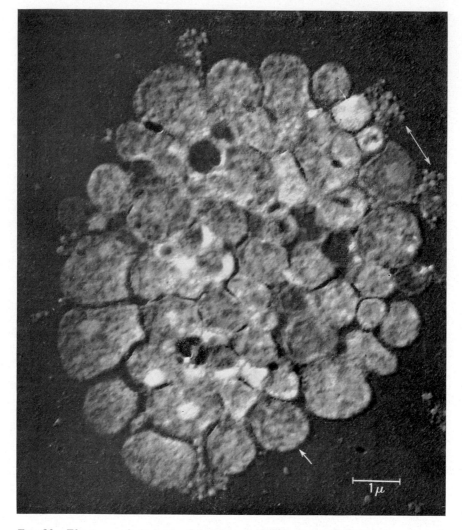

Fig. 23.   Electron micrograph of Laidlaw and Elford's sewage organism, type A grown first at 37°C then at room temperature for 24 hours, shadowed and taken as 21. Note the minimal reproductive units. (First published by Cuckow and Klieneberger-Nobel in 1955).

agalactia; here a great variety of PPLO-cells have produced thin centres and concentrated outer ridges.

A micro-colony of Laidlaw and Elford's sewage organism type A is depicted in Fig. 23 consisting of flat PPLO-cells, some of which show a layer of fine granules, whilst others at the very edge of the colony have disintegrated and their assortment of granules can be seen in small

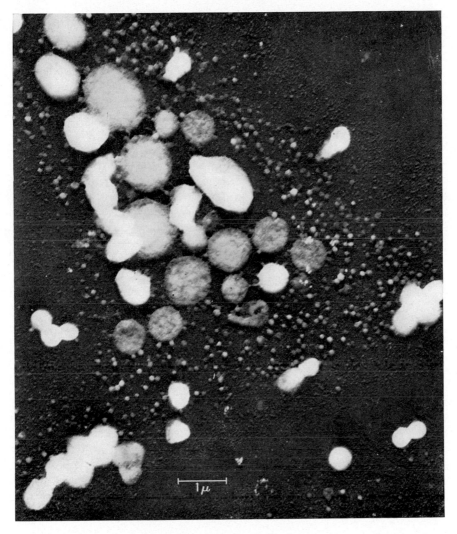

F<small>IG</small>. 24.  Electron micrograph of Laidlaw and Elford's type A sewage organism, shadowed and taken as 21. Note the large amount of minimal reproductive units. (First published by Cuckow and Klieneberger-Nobel, 1955).

packets still kept together by the remains of the cytoplasm. In Fig. 24 a number of PPLO-cells are seen surrounded by an edge of granules set free by disintegration of the mother PPLO-cells. The same organism seen in Fig. 25 shows similar granules as well as PPLO-cells out of which granules have sprouted. These granules are the filterable phase of the organism with a particle size of about 125 m$\mu$ in diameter

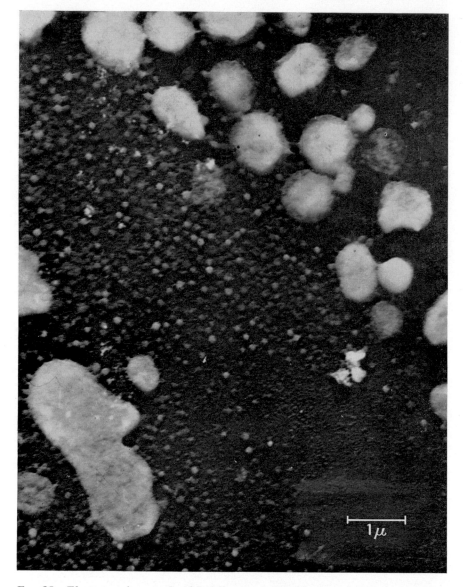

Fɪɢ. 25. Electron micrograph of Laidlaw and Elford's type A sewage organism grown for 15 hours, shadowed and taken as 21. Note minimal reproductive units. (First published by Klieneberger-Nobel in "The Bacteria", Vol. I, 1960. Academic Press, New York and London).

as determined by filtration experiments (see Chapter V). Figure 26 shows a young culture of a rat lung organism from emulsified pus of a lung abscess which was sown in a thin suspension on to a Formvar

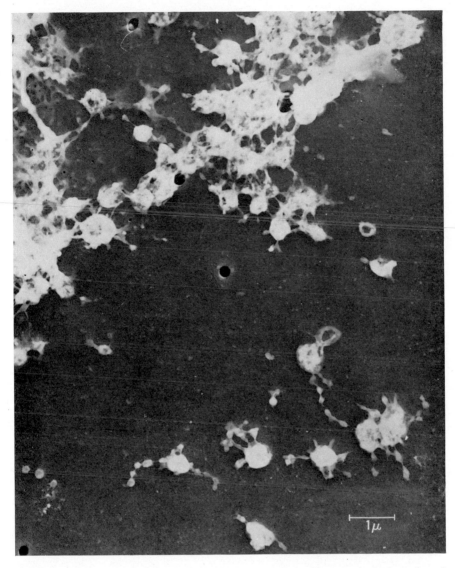

Fig. 26. Electron micrograph of a rat lung organism (from pus) shadowed and taken as 21. Note the filaments and minimal reproductive units. (First published by Klieneberger-Nobel in 1956 and again in 1960a).

membrane. A delightful pattern of cytoplasmic droplets (PPLO-cells) with attached filaments and granules, is seen particularly well in the lower right-hand corner of the photograph.

When the images obtained by the various above methods are com-

pared with the diagram showing the development of PPLO (Fig. 4), it
is seen that the variegated appearances are manifestations of one and
the same growth plan which can be described briefly as follows: A
droplet of cytoplasm developing from a granule, grows, covers the
medium in a thin layer and divides by segmentation, sprouting and
branching into flat PPLO-cells of different sizes and shapes. After a
time a differentiation results in thin and concentrated areas, and often
concentrated ridges of cytoplasm occur at the edges of the cells. The
concentrated cytoplasm produces the minimal reproductive units,
namely the granules which grow again in the same culture to produce
a new generation of elements if sufficient nutrients are available. Some
authors have used the name "elementary corpuscles" for the granules
or minimal reproductive units; this seems a misnomer likely to create
confusion since the elementary bodies of the viruses have different
properties.

## 2. *In Liquid Media*

In all the literature on PPLO no better illustrations can be found of
darkfield preparations of the organism of pleuropneumonia bovis than
those published by Turner in 1935. He achieved this feat with relatively simple microphotographical equipment. In Fig. 27 some of his
illustrations are reproduced which show the similarity of his pictures
with the diagrammatic representations in Figs. 4 and 5. In the first row
of Fig. 27, disks are seen that carry condensed material round the edges
and sometimes a granule. In the following row, filaments and granules
are seen which have developed from the peripheral granules of the
PPLO-cells to which they are still attached. The filaments and asters
thus produced are well illustrated in number 36 of Fig. 27. Figure 28
is a reproduction of one of Turner's photographs (published as Fig. 1,
Plate IV in his 1935 paper) and represents an excellent example of a
filamentous outgrowth of the organism of pleuropneumonia bovis in a
serum broth culture at 24 hours. It shows filaments partly transformed
into strings of small globules and many of the asters so characteristic
for this type of growth.

The best insight into the development of PPLO in fluid medium is
gained from electron micrographs. Figure 29 represents the cells of a
very young culture of the organism of agalactia and shows a phase of
uniform compact round and oval PPLO-cells, measuring about 300 m$\mu$
in diameter, some of which have just started to produce a thin spot in
the centre. Figure 30 shows a more advanced stage in the development of the goat pleuropneumonia organism. Some PPLO-cells are
disk-shaped with a thin centre and a concentrated peripheral layer of
cytoplasm; in others it can be seen how granules have formed within
the ridge; there are also short filamentous forms which have produced

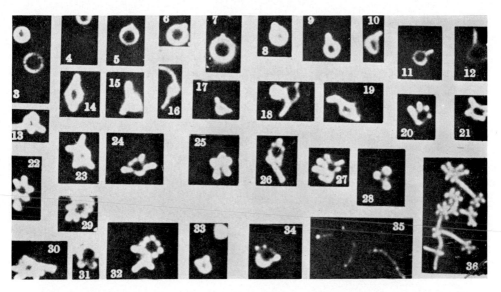

FIG. 27.  The organism of contagious bovine pleuropneumonia from serum broth culture. Photographs of dark field preparations by A. W. Turner, (1935). Figures 3 to 36, Plate III from his article "On the morphology and life cycles" of the organism. Magnification: × 3600.

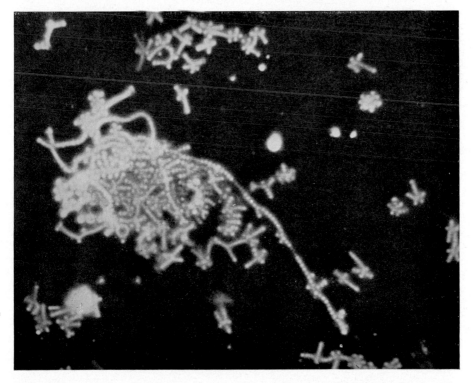

FIG. 28.  The organism of contagious bovine pleuropneumonia from serum broth culture. Photograph of a dark field preparation by A. W. Turner, (1935). Figure 1, Plate IV from his article "On the morphology and life cycles" of this organism. Magnification: × 2520.

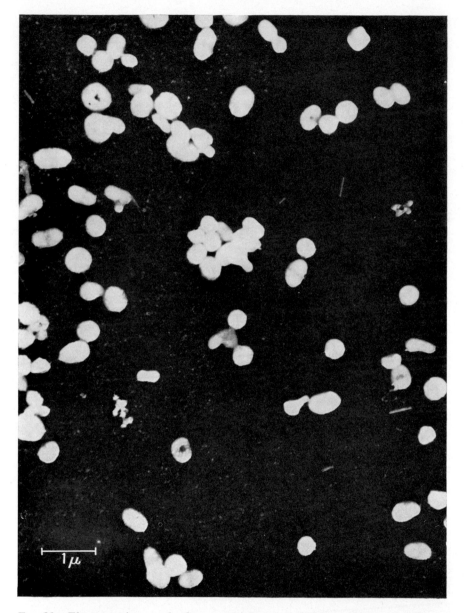

Fig. 29. Electron micrograph of an over-night culture of the organism of agalactia of sheep and goats from liquid medium, shadowed and taken as 21. (First published by Klieneberger-Nobel and Cuckow, 1955). (The small rods are asbestos fibres).

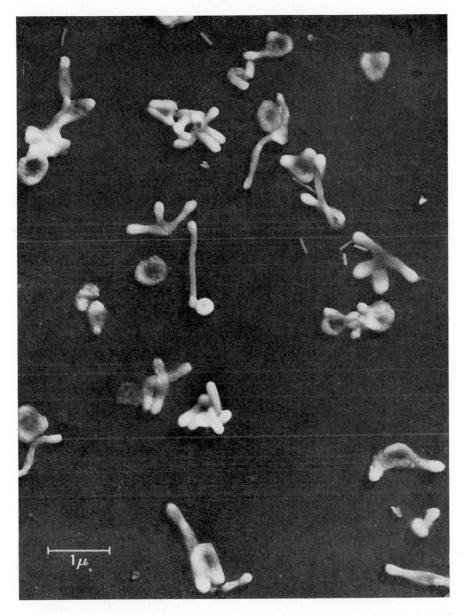

FIG. 30.  Electron micrograph of a 24 hour serum broth culture of the organism of caprine pleuropneumonia shadowed and taken as 21. (First published by Klieneberger-Nobel and Cuckow, 1955). (The small rods are asbestos fibres).

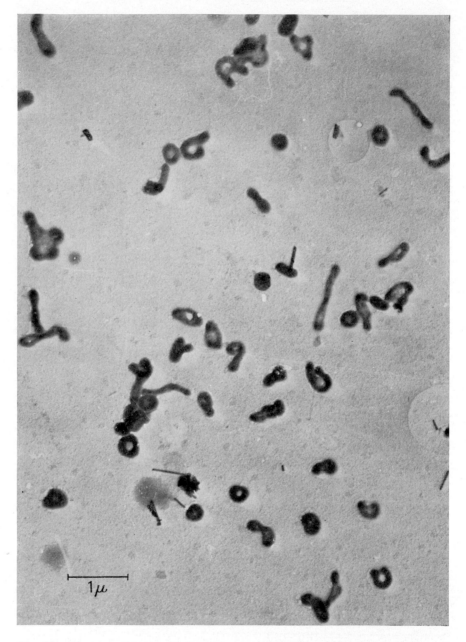

Fig. 31. Electron micrograph of a 24 hour serum broth culture of the organism of caprine pleuropneumonia, shadowed and taken as 21, but directly printed from the negative. (The small rods are asbestos fibres).

granules at their tips. Figure 31 illustrates a large variety of these elements in a picture directly printed from the negative where the detail is fairly well resolved.

The bewildering effect which the various complex aggregates of PPLO-cells may have on the uninitiated disappears completely when, by comparison of the images, the underlying plan of development is understood.

The differences of opinion on the morphology of PPLO seem almost irreconcilable (see *Annals of New York Academy of Sciences*, 1960). They are partly due to the fact that some authors have concentrated mainly on one aspect of growth. Thus Freundt (1960) and Turner (1935, 1959) have been chiefly interested in the study of the organisms in liquid media, whereas Klieneberger-Nobel in her first papers has paid more attention to the development on solid media. Both kinds of media can support the growth of all the organisms excellently, although the type of growth produced appears to be dissimilar. Doubtless there has been a considerable amount of misunderstanding among the opponents in the different camps. Thus Freundt (1960), accuses Klieneberger and Smiles (1942), Klieneberger-Nobel (1956) and Dienes (1960) and Liebermeister (1960) of the strange concept that the "branching filamentous structures do not represent the natural forms of the organisms" and are considered as "artifacts". Nothing could be more wrong, for what these authors believe is that liquid and solid conditions of media influence the growth in different ways. As a result the growth is filamentous and in small forms in the liquid medium, whereas on the solid medium flat PPLO-cells of various sizes and shapes are often produced. I have tried for many years to show that the growth, although different in appearance, follows the same plan of development and that all the various cells and configurations are "natural" manifestations of the organism. When this is understood it will be seen that the differences of appearance are irrelevant and thus the differences of opinion can also be reconciled.

It should be added here that no worker has been able to follow the development of a granule into a colony in a preparation of growing living material, because the granules and some of the elements involved are too small and insubstantial to be resolved in the living state by even the best microscopical equipment. Therefore all accounts of the growth cycle have been based on sequences of images as observed under phase contrast, darkfield microscopy, in stained specimens and electron micrographs, and interpretation and conjecture have been at work in connecting the images obtained and producing a theory of their possible developmental cycle.

Further, it should be pointed out that the demonstration of the phase of minimal reproductive units is not easily achieved. The present

author has shown these small units in various PPLO in stained preparations as well as in electron micrographs. It is my opinion that
multiplication in PPLO occurs widely, though not exclusively, by
means of these units. They are produced in large numbers at certain
stages of development. This peculiar multiplication method seems to
distinguish PPLO from other microbes known to us.

# CHAPTER IV

# Isolation of Pleuropneumonia-like Organisms and their Growth Characteristics

In order to isolate any particular microbe it is necessary to have a suitable source of the organism, a good medium and the correct conditions for growth.

In the following the empirically devised optimal media are described. The studies of the nutritional requirements and metabolism of PPLO are dealt with in Chapter VIII (see also Madoff, 1960).

## A. Organism of Pleuropneumonia and Agalactia

Workers who study pleuropneumonia in cattle use as sources the pleural exudate or, depending on the stage of the disease the spleen, other organs or even the blood of the animals. They usually obtain the organism in pure culture on a meat infusion peptone agar or Turner's V.F. medium (1935) enriched with 5% to 10% horse serum. The colonies develop after two to four days and measure 10-600µ in diameter according to age and distribution on the plate; they do not grow at room temperature but develop at 37°C under aerobic conditions. Under low microscopical power (magnification 30-100 times) they are easily recognized as small round colonies with a darkish centre and a transparent peripheral zone. The smallest colonies may consist of a central zone only. The agent of caprine pleuropneumonia is obtained in a similar way; however, its colonies grow faster and to a larger size than those of bovine pleuropneumonia. Both organisms tend to grow as filaments in liquid media and are therefore well suited for the demonstration of this type of growth as previously mentioned. It has to be realized, however, that their mode of growth is subject to very quick changes and, if it is desired to show their filamentous phase at its best, they have to be caught at the right moment.

The organism of agalactia of sheep and goats is best obtained from the milk or purulent secretion inoculated on to a medium similar to the one used for the organisms of pleuropneumonia. The colonies appearing after two to four days of aerobic incubation are usually a little smaller and show a little more structure than those of pleuropneumonia of cattle and goats; on many media some cultures produce crystals.

## B. Organisms from Rats and Mice

The organisms responsible for diseases in rats and mice are somewhat more difficult to grow than those of pleuropneumonia and agalactia, and I have for many years used the following medium for this purpose. A heart infusion peptone agar is prepared in the orthodox way and from this a "boiled blood medium" is made by adding 5% defibrinated blood of any animal species to the liquefied, cooled (60°C) agar medium. The mixture (not more than one litre at a time to avoid overheating) is boiled up twice in succession and the "chocolate flakes" are eliminated by filtering the medium through Green's 450 filter paper, under sterile conditions in a steam sterilizer at a temperature of about 70°C. The medium is then dispensed, again under sterile conditions, into test tubes (about 15 ml. each) which may finally be reheated in the steamer for 5 to 10 minutes as a last safety measure against contamination. The tubes are kept at 4°C and to liquefy the agar they are heated in boiling water for as short a period as conveniently possible; the pH should be between 7·8 and 8·0. When enriched with 20% horse serum this completed medium seems to contain all the necessary growth factors required by the organisms occurring in rats and mice. The agent of pneumonia in mice and that of bronchopneumonia in rats can thus be grown without difficulty from diseased parts of the lungs. The organism causing polyarthritis in rats can be isolated from synovial fluid, pus produced within the joints, or in severely ill animals, from the spleen, the kidneys, the lymph glands and the blood. The polyarthritis organism usually shows small colonies of granular appearance with pronounced centres, whereas the lung organism produces colonies with a surface structure showing a peripheral part of "lacy appearance" and small, pin-point centres.

## C.   Organisms from Dogs, Cattle and Humans

The media so far described will neither support satisfactorily all the organisms which Chu and Beveridge (1954) have grown from the genitals of dogs, nor all those which Edward (1950) has grown from the genitals of cattle. The same applies to those which have been cultivated from the genitals of humans by many authors (Klieneberger-Nobel, 1960b). Using Edward's suggestion (1954), we prepare our medium, which fulfils the requirements of these organisms, as follows: A "boiled blood medium" as already described serves as a base and to this 0·5% "Oxoid" yeast extract from a 10% stock solution—previously filtered or centrifuged for clarification—as well as 20μg. per ml. of D.N.A.* are added; the medium should have a pH of 7·8 to 8·0 and should be fairly soft. The agar percentage, however, cannot be defined, as various agar preparations often differ widely in gelling power. Finally, serum is added for enrichment and, as organisms from human

---

* Sodium salt of nucleic acid from thymus gland, The British Drug Houses Ltd.

genitals frequently do not tolerate horse serum at first isolation, human serum has to be used for enrichment when it is desired to grow these strains. The medium described is suitable for general purposes of cultivation including maintenance of established cultures. It is sometimes advisable to enrich it further by addition of 1% of a Seitz-filtered staphylococcus broth culture. The saprophytic staphylococcus from which the filtrate is made was isolated as an air contaminant on a plate previously inoculated with a very exacting human PPLO which had only developed as satellite colonies round those of the staphylococcus, but not at a distance from them (see also Morton *et al.* 1949).

When materials from contaminated sources are spread on plates, it is often extremely difficult to obtain colonies well enough isolated for subculture; therefore bacteriostatic substances are now usually incorporated into the isolation media. Those most frequently used are penicillin and thallium acetate (Edward, 1954), the first of which is supposed to keep the gram-positive bacteria down and the second the gram-negative. We add 50 units/ml. of penicillin and 0·25 gr. per litre of thallium acetate to our isolation media. Sterile stock solutions of 10% yeast extract, a 0·2% solution of DNA, a penicillin solution containing 20,000 units/ml. and a 1% thallium acetate solution are maintained.

The plates can be poured conveniently as follows: Place 4 ml. of serum into test tube No. 1, add 0·05 ml. of penicillin (one drop). Test tube No. 2 contains 15 ml. agar medium, add 1 ml. of yeast extract, 0·2 ml. of DNA solution and 0·5 ml. of the thallium acetate solution. Liquify No. 2, cool down to about 50°C, warm No. 1 and pour the plate. If the staphylococcus broth filtrate is required, add 1 ml. to tube No. 1. It is not necessary to dry these plates. We use 9 cm. diameter plates for isolation purposes and 5 cm. diameter plates for maintenance.

## D.  SUBCULTURING PPLO

However good the media may be, the growth is rarely confluent. If the inoculum is rich in viable cells the peripheral zones of colonies may join up and the single dark centres will still be visible with an appearance resembling a number of eggs fried together in one pan. It is advisable, for the subculture of PPLO, to cut out an agar block carrying one or more colonies and to move this over the surface of the new agar plate. A subculture is not always obtained by means of a loop or needle; this is partly due to the tendency of the growth to embed itself into the medium and partly because the organism dies quickly at incubator temperature. Thus liquid cultures may be completely dead after 48 hours at 37°C, and in a colony several days old, many elements may have died. Therefore the tip of a needle may not always strike living elements when pricking a colony. In order to produce the first growth passage in liquid medium, an agar block carrying colonies is transferred to broth which should contain the same constituents as the previously used solid medium; growth is more quickly obtained if the block is squashed. As soon as a pure culture has been procured the bacteriostatic substances can be omitted. Usually the growth in liquid medium consists of a slight but even turbidity, but sometimes it is granular. This may occur because the medium is deficient, but there seem to be some species, such as the rat lung organism, which always grow in small clumps in liquid medium. Many of the PPLO grow better in broth if they are aerated, for example by shaking during incubation. There are, however, a few species such as the organism from the human mouth which prefer anaerobic conditions and grow very feebly or not at all when incubated aerobically. When cultures are grown in bulk in liquid media, it is advisable to cover the bottom of the flask with a thin layer of solid medium and to add the broth when this has solidified. PPLO grow from a very small inoculum. A viable culture grown overnight in the above-described optimal liquid media can be diluted $10^{10}$ to $10^{12}$ times and growth will be obtained from all dilutions. A few colonies will grow on the solid medium and a slight characteristic turbidity will develop after some days from the highest dilution containing only a few organisms.

## E.   Maintenance of PPLO

As mentioned before cultures of PPLO die out quickly at incubation temperature and they also do not survive long at room temperature. When stored at 4°C they remain viable for about a fortnight on solid media; they are more difficult to keep at this temperature in liquid media. However, when they are stored at temperatures of –20°C or lower they stay alive in the broth for 6 to 12 months without subculturing.

Some workers have kept cultures viable in the freeze-dried state for long periods; this method has not worked out well in our hands, although its success may depend on details of the technique used.

# CHAPTER V

# Determination of Particle Size by Filtration

## A. Historical Introduction

Filtration as applied by the bacteriologist serves in the first place as a means for eliminating bacteria from gaseous and liquid substances, and in the second place for determining the particle size of agents smaller than bacteria such as viruses and bacteriophages. The history of bacteriological filtration (see H. Knöll, 1941) takes us back to the middle of the last century when Schröder and van Dusch in 1854 used filtration through cotton wool for the first time in order to keep boiled, sterile liquids free from contamination with air-borne germs, the causes of fermentation and rotting. The first useful bacterial filters for liquids were devised by Pasteur and his pupil, Chamberland. They evolved filters made of porcelain clay in the shape of candles which were fired in such a way that they still retained some porosity. The Chamberland candles were first demonstrated at a session of the "Académie des Sciences" in 1884 and were recommended for the filtration of drinking water suspected of containing bacterial pathogens. In 1891, Nordtmeyer described the first bacterial filters made from infusorial earth (silicious earth), the type that became later known as Berkefeld filters (Bitter, 1891). Another substance used for the sterilization of liquids by filtration is asbestos. In 1915, during the first world war, disks of this material serving to sterilize drinking water were processed by the Seitz-Werke in Germany. The "E.K." disks (Entkeimungsscheiben, sterilization disks) made to the present day by the firm of Seitz are used in all bacteriological laboratories for the sterilization of liquids such as serum, sugar solutions, etc., which are easily destroyed or decomposed by heat. The disks assembled in the filterholder can be autoclaved and are used only once.

Another fairly new development are the sintered glass filters: they were developed by P. H. Prausnitz (1930) and first produced by Schott and Genossen in Jena (Germany) in 1935. They are made from "Geräteglas" powders which are heated to such a degree that an incomplete sintering of the glass particles takes place; they can be produced in different porosities. Usually, a sintered layer of fine porosity "G 5" is superimposed on a supporting, coarser layer "G 3", a type of filter designated G 5/3. The two combined layers are melted into suitably shaped glass mantels and each filter is tested for its porosity. The advantage of these filters is that they can be autoclaved, cleaned with acids and water and repeatedly used without changes in their porosity; however, they cannot be finely graded like membrane filters.

The production of membrane filters from organic substances such as cellulose derivatives, meant another big step forward in filtration technique, for they were the first filters in which pore diameter, rather than adsorption, was responsible for their ability to retain or to filter particles.

## B.  Ultra-filtration Analysis

A number of different filters are now available for the elimination of bacteria and sterilization by filtration, but when the aim is the determination of particle size of dispersed agents smaller than bacteria, only membrane filters are suitable. The process of sieving small particles through membranes of different porosities for the determination of their sizes is called ultra-filtration analysis. Good, non-volatile solvents such as acetic acid, or volatile solvents such as mixtures of alcohol and ether, can be employed in preparing the collodion solution. If the acetic acid collodion method is adopted filter paper disks can be impregnated with acetic acid collodion and gelled in water: this method was first used by Bechhold (1907). In the second method a suitable concentration of nitro cellulose in alcohol–ether provides a solution of low viscosity; this is quickly poured on to a flat glass cell to form a gel film of the desired properties. By this method collodion membranes of sufficient strength can be obtained which need no support. According to Elford (1938) the acetic acid collodion membranes are not very uniform in porosity and are therefore not suitable for the determination of particle sizes. In contrast, alcohol–ether membranes are not only strong but also uniform; however, they cannot be produced over a wide range of porosities. In 1931 Elford invented a method for producing collodion membranes of graded porosity. If a combination of acetone and amyl alcohol with ethyl alcohol and ether is used as solvent, the aggregation can be repressed by the addition of small percentages of a good solvent such as acetic acid; thus membranes of lower porosities are obtained. On the other hand, porosity can be raised by adding a non-solvent like water. Thus graded membranes with porosities ranging from 10 m$\mu$ to 3 $\mu$ can be prepared. For convenience sake these membranes have been called "gradocol membranes". The details of their production, their properties as well as methods for their calibration, are found in Elford's invaluable article on the sizes of viruses and bacteriophages (1938). These membranes are excellent for the determination of sizes because their average pore diameter (a.p.d.) is close to their maximal pore diameter, and because they can be produced in such a wide range of porosities. They used to be available from the Wright-Fleming Institute, St. Mary's Hospital, London.

For ultra-filtration analysis a series of membranes of graded uniformity and reproducibility, exhibiting stability and strength and chemical inertness must be available. Gradocol membranes answer these specifications. A knowledge of the principles of ultra-filtration as well as of the relationship between the porosity of the limiting membrane and the size of the particles is also required. Filtration through a collodion membrane is not a simple sieving. Attention has to be paid to such factors as adsorption and blocking of the pores, because the capillaries through which filtration proceeds may be 100 times as long as wide and quite irregular in their course. Therefore the suspension filtered must be almost clear and free from foreign particles; the amount filtered must not be too small because only after some intitial adsorption does the filtration proper get under way. The time of filtration must not be too long, for once the filter is blocked, it no longer acts as a sieve. The pressure, positive or negative, must be adequate and in a certain relationship to the porosity of the filter; if it is too high particles may be pressed or pulled through instead of being filtered. Furthermore, the results are only significant if the dispersed phase is rich in viable particles; a suspension of too low a viable particle count may be completely adsorbed and therefore too high an endpoint of filtration will be obtained. Finally, the temperature, the composition and reaction of the medium that contains the dispersed phase, are important factors, since they affect filtration by their influence on the viscosity of the filtrants.

The size of the particles is calculated by means of a simple equation. The average pore diameter "d" of the membrane just completely retaining all the particles is known as the "filtration endpoint". From experimentally established filtration curves it can be seen that by adopting a factor F the particle diameter "p" is determined by the relationship $p = F.d$ (Elford, 1938). The factor F can be read from the following Table :

| Limiting pore diameter, d, in mμ | Factor F |
|---|---|
| 10–100 | 0.30–0.50 |
| 100–500 | 0.50–0.75 |
| 500–1000 | 0.75–1.0 |

## C. Ultra-filtration Analysis Applied to PPLO and L-forms of Bacteria

The L-form of bacteria is included here because the filtration experiments discussed have been carried out with both groups of organisms and have yielded valuable information.

The ultra-filtration method has been widely used for the determination of the particle sizes of viruses and bacteriophages. It was applied by Elford in 1938 to measure the sizes of the minimal reproductive units of the organisms of pleuropneumonia, agalactia and sewage organisms. As mentioned in Bordet's paper (1910), Dujardin-Beaumetz had already filtered the organism of bovine pleuropneumonia through Berkefeld and Chamberland filters more than 50 years ago.

The final aim of the experiments carried out in my laboratory was first of all to find the endpoints of filtration and secondly, to determine the numbers of particles per ml. which passed the filters.

## 1. *Methods*

Jena glass filters, G 5/3, and gradocol membranes of different a.p.d. were used. As it was desired to compare the filterability of various organisms the glass filters were useful, because the same filter could be used repeatedly for the filtration of different suspensions; however, for the ultra-filtration analysis and the determination of endpoints, gradocol membranes were exclusively used.

As pointed out above, certain rules have to be followed in filtration experiments; the suspensions for filtration were well dispersed and almost clear though as rich in viable particles as possible; the negative or positive pressure applied was low and sufficiently large volumes were filtered. When membranes with a small a.p.d. were used, fractionated filtration was carried out in order to eliminate the larger particles.

The cultures were transferred daily for a week to obtain optimal growth in the liquid medium. They were spun in an angle centrifuge at 4000 r.p.m. for one hour. The sediment was resuspended in a few ml. of serum broth and thoroughly ground in a Griffith tube, and the resulting emulsion was made up to the original volume by the addition of serum broth. A second short centrifugation was carried out and the resulting clear, or almost clear, supernatant was used for the filtration. The gradocol membranes had a diameter of 3 cm., the filtered amount was at least 15 ml., the filtration time 5–20 min. according to the porosity of the filter and the positive or negative pressure corresponded to the pressure of a 10 cm. mercury column. The end titres were determined by diluting the suspensions and the filtrates in a series of tenfold dilutions (transferring 0·5 ml. each time to 4·5 ml. of sterile serum broth) and incubating the dilutions at 37°C for 10 days.

## 2. *Organisms*

### PPLO

Organism of agalactia of sheep and goats; the "rolling disease" agent; Laidlaw and Elford's sewage organism, type A; the organisms of pleuropneumonia of goats and cattle.

## Stable L-forms of Bacteria

"L 1 rat 30" = L-form of *Streptobacillus moniliformis*, maintained in culture for 20 years.
"L Fair" = L-form of *Fusiformis necrophorus*, strain 132 of Dienes, maintained 6 years.
"L 1 An" = L-form of *Streptobacillus moniliformis*, maintained 6 years.

## 3. *Results*

Table I shows the results of a typical filtration; the organism of agalactia was filtered through a Jena glass filter. The original suspension contained not less than $10^{11}$ and the filtrate not less than $10^8$ viable elements in 0·5 ml. liquid. Consequently 0·1% of the corpuscles passed the filter (see Fig. 32).

Tables II and III show the results of filtrations carried out with various PPLO and L-forms of bacteria. Table II summarises all the filtrations through Jena glass filters, Table III all those through gradocol membranes. On the left side of each table the experiments with PPLO are listed, those with L-forms are on the right. The columns headed A show the titres of the suspensions, the columns headed B those of the filtrates. The last column on each side headed B/A × 100, shows the percentages of viable elements which passed the filters. Table II shows that 3 times in 17 filtration experiments 100% of the PPLO particles had passed the filters, once 10%, 6 times 1%, and 3 times 0·1%. On only three occasions did less than 0·1% pass the filters. One filtrate contained no viable particles at all, but in this case the suspension was quite unsuitable as it contained only 100 viable particles per ml. When it is realized that the number of viable elements varies in the suspensions and that elements of different sizes are present which may form aggregates, varying results must be expected, even though the glass filters have a relatively high a.p.d.

If the results obtained with the two groups of organisms are compared, it is seen that the number of particles in the L-suspensions and L-filtrates are of a much lower order than those in the PPLO suspensions and filtrates. The reduction of particle numbers by means of filtration through the Jena glass filters is altogether much greater in the L-forms than in the PPLO.

Table III shows the filtration experiments with gradocol membranes. The a.p.d. in mμ are listed in the second column; under A and B the titres of the suspensions and filtrates are tabulated. Membranes varying between 910 and 200 mμ a.p.d. were used in 11 filtration experiments with the organism of agalactia. The endpoint of filtration was at 290 mμ. Therefore, according to Elford's formula, the diameter of the smallest particles of agalactia measured 145 to 217 mμ. Elford obtained

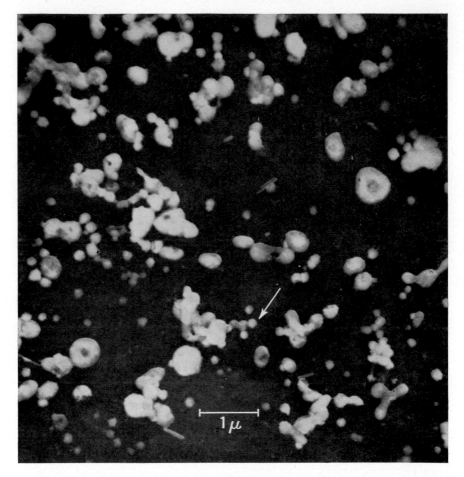

Fig. 32.  Electron micrograph of a suspension of particles of the organism of agalactia of sheep and goats which had passed a sintered glass filter. Note the minimal reproductive units and the larger PPLO-cells. (First published by Klieneberger-Nobel in 1956).

the values of 150–225 mμ in his experiments, a very close agreement.

However, in these 11 experiments, suspensions prepared as described have been used without prefiltration and these still contained a considerable number of particles which could not pass the finer membranes and must have had a blocking effect. If more exact results are desired suspensions previously filtered through a filter of medium a.p.d. should be used for experiments with the finer membranes. The lower part of Table III shows the results with such prefiltered suspensions. Now the endpoint of filtration is at 240 mμ a.p.d. If Elford's formula is applied, a diameter of 120–180 mμ is obtained for the minimal repro-

## TABLE I

RESULTS OF A FILTRATION OF THE ORGANISM OF AGALACTIA THROUGH A JENA GLASS FILTER

| Dilution | Suspension | | | | Filtrate | | | |
|---|---|---|---|---|---|---|---|---|
| | 1 day | 3 days | 6 days | 10 days | 1 day | 3 days | 6 days | 10 days |
| $10^1$ | +++ | +++ | +++ | +++ | +++ | +++ | +++ | +++ |
| $10^2$ | + | +++ | +++ | +++ | + | +++ | +++ | +++ |
| $10^3$ | | +++ | +++ | +++ | | +++ | +++ | +++ |
| $10^4$ | | ++ | +++ | +++ | | | +++ | +++ |
| $10^5$ | | + | +++ | +++ | | | +++ | +++ |
| $10^6$ | | | +++ | +++ | | | +++ | +++ |
| $10^7$ | | | +++ | +++ | | | | +++ |
| $10^8$ | | | +++ | +++ | | | | +++ |
| $10^9$ | | | +++ | +++ | | | | |
| $10^{10}$ | | | +++ | +++ | | | | |
| $10^{11}$ | | | | +++ | | | | |
| $10^{12}$ | | | | | | | | |

+ = hardly turbid, ++ = clearly turbid, +++ = completely developed

## TABLE II

FILTRATIONS OF PPLO AND L-FORMS THROUGH JENA FILTERS

| Organism | Titre A | Titre B | B/A × 100 | Organism | Titre A | Titre B | B/A × 100 |
|---|---|---|---|---|---|---|---|
| Agalactia sheep | $10^{10}$ | $10^{10}$ | 100 | L1rat 30 | $10^7$ | $10^6$ | 10 |
| Agalactia sheep | $10^{10}$ | $10^{10}$ | 100 | L1rat 30 | $10^8$ | $10^6$ | 1 |
| Agalactia sheep | $10^{10}$ | $10^{10}$ | 100 | L1rat 30 | $10^9$ | $10^6$ | 0·1 |
| Agalactia sheep | $10^9$ | $10^8$ | 10 | L1rat 30 | $10^8$ | $10^3$ | 0·001 |
| Agalactia sheep | $10^{11}$ | $10^9$ | 1 | L1rat 30 | $10^8$ | $10^1$ | 0·00001 |
| Agalactia sheep | $10^{11}$ | $10^9$ | 1 | L1rat 30 | $10^9$ | $10^2$ | 0·00001 |
| Agalactia sheep | $10^{10}$ | $10^8$ | 1 | L1 An | $10^8$ | $10^4$ | 0·01 |
| Agalactia sheep | $10^{10}$ | $10^8$ | 1 | L Fair | $10^6$ | $10^3$ | 0·1 |
| Agalactia sheep | $10^8$ | $10^6$ | 1 | L Fair | $10^7$ | 0 | 0 |
| Agalactia sheep | $10^7$ | $10^5$ | 1 | | | | |
| Agalactia sheep | $10^{11}$ | $10^8$ | 0·1 | | | | |
| Agalactia sheep | $10^9$ | $10^6$ | 0·1 | | | | |
| Agalactia sheep | $10^{11}$ | $10^6$ | 0·001 | | | | |
| Pleuropneumonia goat | $10^9$ | $10^6$ | 0·1 | | | | |
| Pleuropneumonia goat | $11^{11}$ | $10^7$ | 0·01 | | | | |
| Rolling disease mouse | $10^7$ | $10^3$ | 0·01 | | | | |
| Sewage organism | $10^8$ | $10^3$ | 0·001 | | | | |
| Pleuropneumonia cattle | $10^2$ | 0 | 0 | | | | |

ductive units of agalactia, a value probably nearer the truth when we take into account that the minimal reproductive units measure only 100 m$\mu$ in the electron micrographs.

## TABLE III

FILTRATIONS OF PPLO AND L-FORMS THROUGH GRADOCOL MEMBRANES

| Organism | a.p.d. in mμ | Titre A | Titre B | B/A X 100 | Organism | a.p.d. in mμ | Titre A | Titre B | B/A X 100 |
|---|---|---|---|---|---|---|---|---|---|
| Agalactia sheep | 910 | $10^9$ | $10^9$ | 100 | Llrat 30 | 910 | $10^8$ | $10^6$ | 1 |
| Agalactia sheep | 650 | $10^{10}$ | $10^9$ | 10 | Llrat 30 | 660 | $10^8$ | $10^3$ | 0·001 |
| Agalactia sheep | 560 | $10^9$ | $10^8$ | 10 | Llrat 30 | 660 | $10^5$ | 0 | 0 |
| Agalactia sheep | 560 | $10^9$ | $10^7$ | 1 | Llrat 30 | 600 | $10^9$ | $10^2$ | 0·00001 |
| Agalactia sheep | 420 | $10^7$ | $10^4$ | 0·1 | L Fair | 600 | $10^6$ | 0 | 0 |
| Agalactia sheep | 420 | $10^9$ | $10^6$ | 0·1 | Prot L 9 | 590 | $10^8$ | $10^3$ | 0·001 |
| Agalactia sheep | 300 | $10^{10}$ | $10^6$ | 0·01 | Prot L 9 | 590 | $10^9$ | $10^3$ | 0·0001 |
| Agalactia sheep | 290 | $10^{10}$ | 0 | 0 | Prot L 9 | 500 | $10^8$ | 10 | 0·00001 |
| Agalactia sheep | 290 | $10^{10}$ | 0 | 0 | L Fair | 500 | $10^6$ | 0 | 0 |
| Agalactia sheep | 200 | $10^{10}$ | 0 | 0 | Llrat 30 | 500 | $10^8$ | 10 | 0·00001 |
| Agalactia sheep | 200 | $10^{10}$ | 0 | 0 | Llrat 30 | 500 | $10^8$ | 0 | 0 |
| | | | | | Llrat 30 | 450 | $10^8$ | 0 | 0 |

Agalactia sheep suspension prefiltered through Jena filters

| a.p.d. in mμ | Titre A | Titre B | B/A X 100 |
|---|---|---|---|
| 430 | $10^6$ | $10^5$ | 10 |
| 430 | $10^8$ | $10^5$ | 0·1 |
| 430 | $10^9$ | $10^3$ | 0·0001 |
| 390 | $10^{10}$ | $10^2$ | 0·000001 |
| 340 | $10^5$ | $10^2$ | 0·1 |
| 340 | $10^8$ | $10^2$ | 0·0001 |
| 340 | $10^9$ | $10^2$ | 0·00001 |
| 240 | $10^{10}$ | $10^2$ | 0·000001 |
| 240 | $10^8$ | 0 | 0 |
| 240 | $10^{10}$ | 0 | 0 |

The results of the filtration experiments with L-forms of bacteria are different. Filters having an a.p.d. of 500 mμ sometimes still allowed L-particles to pass, but filters of 450 mμ and finer pores produced sterile filtrates. In earlier experiments an occasional positive result had been obtained with membranes of 400 mμ a.p.d. (particle size 175-250 mμ) (Klieneberger-Nobel, 1949, 1951). If now the filtration endpoint of 450 mμ a.p.d. is taken, a diameter measuring 225–337 mμ is obtained for the smallest particles. The difference between the filterability of the PPLO and the L-forms of bacteria seems very much more remarkable if the numbers of particles in the filtrates are compared. From Table III it can be seen that the number of filtered agalactia particles was much larger than the number of filtered L-form particles in similar experiments. Indeed, the electron micrographs confirm this difference, for the minimal reproductive units are observed in electron micrographs as granules of uniform size and appearance occurring in large numbers, whereas in the L-forms the small corpuscles seem to vary in size and are less numerous.

# CHAPTER VI

# Chicken Coccobacilliform Bodies and Pleuropneumonia-like Organisms

The criteria for the definition of PPLO used by various authors, as for example those in Sabin's review of 1939, are vague and therefore do not exclude organisms which, in the present author's opinion, do not belong to this group. A more precise definition seems necessary which can now be given after the discussion of the morphology and growth in the preceeding chapters. I suggest the following definition which uses morphological as well as cultural characteristics.

## A. DEFINITION OF PLEUROPNEUMONIA-LIKE ORGANISMS

### 1. On the Basis of Morphological Features

PPLO start their development from single granules (the minimal reproductive units) of a diameter of approximately 125 m$\mu$. These granules are filterable through gradocol membranes with an average pore diameter of 0·24 to 0·3 $\mu$ and they can be demonstrated and measured by means of the electron microscope. A granule grows into a larger PPLO cell which eventually produces within its boundaries concentrated arcas and areas of a thinner appearance. The concentrated areas can be peripherally situated and then appear as solid ridges. New minimal reproductive units are produced within all these areas of consolidation. The organisms of the PPLO group lack a solid cell wall, and therefore their elements often show considerable softness and pleomorphism.

### 2. On the Basis of Growth Characteristics

PPLO produce slight turbidity or granularity in the liquid medium. On solid media characteristic small colonies are produced which have as a rule a dark centre and a transparent peripheral zone; they vary in size between 10 and 600 $\mu$ depending on the time of incubation, the medium and the density of the inoculum. The dark centre of the typical colony is due to a downward growth of the organisms which embed themselves in the agar medium thus producing super-imposed layers of growth.

This definition will be found to exclude organisms which, in my opinion, have so far been wrongly classified or confused with PPLO; they may fulfil one or more but not all of these criteria.

## B. DISCOVERY OF THE COCCOBACILLIFORM BODIES

The coccobacilliform bodies have some properties in common with the PPLO but are in other respects distinct. They were discovered by

Nelson as early as 1935 when he was studying an infectious fowl coryza which is characterized by a slow onset and a long duration. There exists also in the fowl a coryza of rapid onset with a short incubation period of only one to two days. This is caused by the bacterium, *Haemophilus gallinarum* (De Blieck, 1942, 1948, 1950). The chronic coryza of slow onset has an incubation period of 2 to 3 weeks and the nasal discharge persists for two months or longer. Investigating the bacteria-free exudates of the coryza of slow onset Nelson (1936a, b, c, d) observed the constant occurence of minute, gram negative coccal bodies that usually were extracellular, but occasionally intracellularly arranged, both in phagocytes and in epithelial cells; he designated these elements coccobacilliform bodies.

Nelson (1936b) describes them as follows: "The coccobacilliform bodies are minute immobile cells which may be found as single or double units and in aggregates varying from a few cells up to large compact masses of innumerable units. In shape they are commonly spherical but may be slightly elongated, appearing as extremely short bacilli. In size they are generally under $0.5$ $\mu$ and may be so minute that they are barely visible. In exudate removed early in the disease the bodies are usually quite uniform in size. Their detection in films requires a rather intense stain. For routine purposes the Gram stain, counter-staining for several minutes with carbolfuchsin diluted 1:4 with water, has proved highly satisfactory. The individual cells stain deeply and stand out sharply." The usual method for staining smears of sinus exudate is now by Giemsa solution after fixation with methyl alcohol.

## C.　Characteristics of Coccobacilliform Bodies

Though the filterability of the coccobacilliform bodies has not been properly investigated so far, Nelson points out that in his experiments they did not pass the usual Berkefeld V filters, although they did pass through a certain V filter which was also permeable to *Haemophilus gallinarum*. This seems to indicate that granules such as the minimal reproductive units of the PPLO are not present in coccobacilliform body cultures. Moreover, at no developmental stage is there a differentiation into concentrated and thin areas followed by granule formation as in the PPLO, and it seems therefore that multiplication is not by minimal reproductive units but rather by fission. The coccobacilliform bodies are gram-negative and can, unlike PPLO, be deeply stained by Nelson's Gram technique. It would thus appear that they have a surface more like that of a bacterium than of PPLO, although investigations to determine whether they possess a cell wall like bacteria or a "plasmalemma" (Ruska and Poppe, 1947) like PPLO have

not been carried out as yet. The growth appearance of coccobacilliform bodies is slightly different from that of PPLO. Two established
laboratory strains grow with a little more turbidity than PPLO strains
in my liquid medium; on solid media their colonies are approximately
the same size or smaller than those of PPLO, but the differentiation
into a central and peripheral part is less marked. Their regular fine
coccal appearance is well illustrated in Fig. 33.

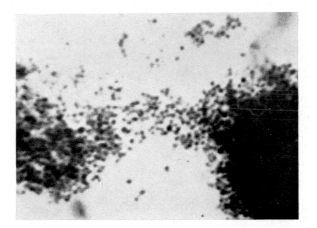

FIG. 33. Coccobacilliform bodies (T strain of Shepard) stained gram according
to Nelson. Magnification: × 1800.

### D. PATHOGENICITY OF COCCOBACILLIFORM BODIES

It is interesting that Nelson's coccobacilliform bodies represent organisms which are not only much smaller than ordinary bacteria, but
which also resemble PPLO in some respects but not in others. The fact
that they are pathogenic should make them of greater interest to bacteriologists. Nelson who discovered them was also the first to demonstrate their pathogenicity (1936d). He successfully cultured the chicken
coryza bodies in fertile eggs and in chick embryo tissue and inoculated
the infected foetal egg membranes and tissue culture suspensions into
the palatine cleft of healthy chickens. These birds developed typical
coryza and the coccobacilliform bodies—not found in healthy chickens
—could be demonstrated in the nasal passages of the diseased birds.
The medium used by Nelson in 1939 had the following composition:
75 mg. of finely minced 10 day chick embryo tissue suspended in 5 ml.
of Seitz-filtered Tyrode solution in 15 mm. test tubes. According to
Nelson the organisms do not need tissue cells for their growth, but do
require a diffusible cellular component for their first multiplication.
Up to 1954 very few workers on avian chronic respiratory disease

(C.R.D.) differentiated between pathogenic coccobacilliform body strains and non-pathogenic PPLO. Any PPLO found in this disease condition was wrongly named *Mycoplasma gallinarum*. Further confusion was caused by Gianforte *et al.* (1955) who reported that 7 "PPLO strains" were serologically identical although they represented in reality different species; the techniques were faulty in this case.

In 1954 Chu confirmed Nelson's findings by demonstrating the coccobacilliform bodies in all cases of fowl coryza of slow onset and C.R.D. of chickens investigated; he pointed out that saprophytic PPLO and pathogenic coccobacilliform bodies occurred simultaneously in this syndrome.

Since 1957 more and more evidence has been brought forward to show that the coccobacilliform bodies of Nelson are the aetiological agents of the chicken coryza of slow onset and the C.R.D. Adler and his collaborators (Adler *et al.* 1957; Adler *et al.* 1958; Yamamoto and Adler, 1958) have differentiated various strains by serological, cultural, morphological and biochemical methods and have come to the conclusion that the pleomorphic PPLO are saprophytes and that the monomorphic coccobacilliform body strains are pathogens. Adler's "56" strain of coccobacilliform bodies from turkeys has now been recognized as the typical example of the haemagglutinating, pathogenic organism throughout the United States and is even manufactured as an antigen for testing the sera of chicken and turkey flocks in the United States. However, this and various other commercial antigens are according to Chu and Newnham (personal communication) unsatisfactory, as they have a tendency to aggregate. Hammer *et al.* (1958) pointed out the many difficulties encountered in serological field tests. Diagnosis is more reliably established by the study of the disease history, the epidemiology and particularly by the demonstration of the coccobacilliform bodies in smears and by culture*. The very important fact that coccobacilliform bodies but not PPLO haemagglutinate chicken erythrocytes, was already known to Fahey and Crawley in 1954. They described a haemagglutination inhibition test and with its help controlled the chicken C.R.D. in Canada (see also Fahey and Crawly, 1956, Crawley and Fahey, 1957 and Crawley, 1960). These workers thus confirmed Chu's findings of 1954, namely, that the coccobacilliform bodies are the sole cause of C.R.D. in chickens.

Workers such as Chu and Newnham (1959), Kleckner (1960) and Moore *et al.* (1960), who have tested serologically many avian coccobacilliform body strains from various countries, have unanimously come to the conclusion that all the pathogenic strains causing coryza

---

*Chu and Newnham recommend for the growth of the coccobacilliform bodies the "Brucella medium" made by Albimi Laboratories (Brooklyn, New York), with the addition of 15% horse serum.

TABLE IV

DIFFERENTIAL DIAGNOSIS OF COCCOBACILLIFORM BODIES AND PPLO FROM CHICKENS

|  | Growth | Morphology | Diameter of smallest particles | Haemagglu-tination |
|---|---|---|---|---|
| Coccobacilli-form bodies | Small colony often no definite centre | Coccobacilli-form | about 250mμ | positive |
| PPLO | Small colony<br><br>Central zone well developed | Very pleo-morphic, ring forms | about 125 mμ | negative |

of slow onset, C.R.D. and turkey sinusitis belong to one serotype and that they possess a common antigen not shared by the non-pathogenic PPLO types.

Table IV shows how chicken coccobacilliform bodies and PPLO may be distinguished from each other.

In 1937 (a, b, c) and 1940 (a, b), Nelson described the occurrence of coccobacilliform bodies in mice and rats and held them responsible for some of the catarrhal and middle ear infections frequently afflicting these rodents. Nobody has so far repeated Nelson's experiments. In my laboratory, coccobacilliform body strains have not as yet been culti-vated from rats and mice. As Nelson himself states that the strains he obtained from rats and mice were more pleomorphic than those from chickens, it seems possible that he was dealing in this case with PPLO and not with coccobacilliform bodies. It is hoped that further studies will clarify the position (see also Nelson 1948, 1949 a, b).

# CHAPTER VII

# Similarities and Differences between Pleuropneumonia-like Organisms and L-Forms* of Bacteria

A short report on the discovery and nature of L-forms serves as an introduction to this chapter (see also Klieneberger-Nobel in "The Bacteria", Vol. I, 1960).

## A. L-FORM OF BACTERIA

Bacteria occur usually in definite shapes, viz. as bacilli, cocci, vibrios and spirilla. Irregularly shaped forms have, however, been observed by most workers since the first era of bacteriology. They occur frequently in freshly isolated cultures as well as in old laboratory strains but are rarely found in repeatedly transferred strains designated "normal cultures" ("normierte Kulturen") by Max Neisser (1926). The irregular pleomorphic forms were regarded as degenerate "involution forms" by a number of workers; others attributed a special significance to them. Thus Kuhn (1927, 1929) believed that they were not of bacterial origin but represented cells of protozoa living as symbionts or parasites in the bacterial cultures. Other bacteriologists such as Almquist (1922), Enderlein (1925), Mellon (1925) and Hadley (1926), regarded them as phases in a bacterial life cycle comprising very small granular forms ("gonidia") and large fusion forms ("zygotes"). Löhnis (1921) held the view that bacteria can exist in a "protoplasmic" stage in which they can combine to form a "symplasma". To support his views he published a great number of tables with innumerable photographs of pleomorphic bacteria. The theories mentioned were probably conceived by the authors in order to explain the regeneration of genetical material in bacteria; for recombination, induced mutation and transduction, were as yet undreamed of in those days.

Many of the earlier workers had already found that the conditions of culture were responsible for the occurrence of pleomorphism. Thus Gamaleia (1900) and Maassen (1904) observed that high salt concentration induced the production of these forms, while Hadley and Almquist found that lithium chloride and low incubation temperatures had the same effect. (For the literature up to 1930 see Klieneberger, 1930).

In 1935 I obtained for the first time a pure culture of protoplasmatic forms of various sizes and shapes from a strain of *Streptobacillus monili-*

* "Formation L" in French, "L-phase" in German (see "L-form" of bacteria in *Nature*, **179**, 461 (1957)).

*formis*. This apparently pure culture reverted at first to bacteria but after a number of transfers remained permanently free from them. I designated *stable strains* of that type, which I later also obtained from other bacteria, as *L-forms* and the particular culture from *Streptobacillus moniliformis* as L 1; (L stands for Lister Institute). Similar cultures were derived by me from the anaerobe *Fusiformis necrophorus* (syn. *Bacteroides*), *Salmonella typhimurium*, *Proteus vulgaris* and an organism similar to *Listeria* which produces disease in small rodents in the Transvaal and was sent to me by Dr. C. Amies (now Toronto, Canada). At the time of my first discovery of the L-form, I was struck by the similarity of its colonies to those of the organism of pleuropneumonia bovis and I tentatively promoted the theory that the L-form was a PPLO which lived as a symbiont with the bacteria. I soon found that whereas the L-form could always be obtained in pure culture, the bacteria could never be purified in such a way that they remained free from the L-form. Other authors, foremost among them Louis Dienes (1939, Dienes and Smith, 1942), proved that the L-form was derived from the bacteria. He demonstrated in convincing pictures of growing cultures how this transformation took place, step by step, and he also showed how the unstable L-form reverted. Today all workers in this field are convinced that the L-form is derived from the bacteria, and *we designate with the letter "L" the growth form which no longer reverts*. Its precursor, similar in macroscopical and light microscopical appearance and still capable of producing bacteria, is called the "transition form" or, by some authors, the "unstable L-form". It appears from chemical studies carried out with L- and transition forms that the former contain no cell wall substances, or negligible amounts of them, whereas the latter still contain an appreciable amount (Weibull, 1958; Weibull and Beckman, 1960; Kandler and Zehender, 1957; Kandler *et al.* 1958; Kandler and Kandler, 1960).

The L-form develops spontaneously in some cultures as for example in *Streptobacillus moniliformis*. In other cultures L-form production can be induced by various substances of which penicillin seems to be the most effective. Dienes has used this antibiotic widely in order to obtain L-forms from a great variety of bacteria. Some amino acids have a similar effect, particularly glycine. A high concentration of common salt was used in addition to penicillin by Sharp (1954) and Dienes and Sharp (1955) to grow L-forms from haemolytic streptococci.

The type of colony produced on solid medium is the most characteristic feature of an L-form strain. These L-colonies, with their dark centres and their lighter peripheral zones exhibiting a coarse lace-like structure, grow in two to three days on a suitable medium to the size of streptococcal colonies and can be seen by naked eye inspection; their finer structure can, however, be seen only under the low power of the microscope (magnification × 30–100). Most strains grow in large clumps or flakes in liquid medium. The L-form of Proteus, however grows diffusely and produces a thick veil ("Kahmhaut" in German) on the surface of the liquid medium.

The biochemical reactions of the L-forms are the same as those of the parent bacteria, although they usually occur more slowly. Yet there is a difference in one respect, viz. L-form strains are not inhibited by penicillin and sulphonamides, whereas their parent bacteria are more or less sensitive to these substances. As the chemists have shown, this property is due to the differences in their surfaces. Both bacteria and L-forms have cytoplasmic membranes, but the bacteria are further enclosed by a solid cell wall that is lacking in the L-form.

Serological investigations have shown that a close antigenic relationship exists between the L-form and its mother bacterium. Certain aberrations which occur can again be explained by surface differences.

It has usually been found that L-forms of pathogenic bacteria are non-pathogenic. It seems possible that in some organisms toxicity of the L-form can be demonstrated (vibrios, clostridia), although more research is necessary on the pathogenicity of the various L-forms (see Klieneberger-Nobel, 1958, 1960a).

## B.   COMPARISON BETWEEN PPLO AND L-FORMS

We will now compare PPLO and L-forms of bacteria in order to find out if their similarities or their differences are of greater significance. The similarity that strikes most workers when they first become acquainted with both sorts of culture is the type of colony which in both is differentiated into a central dark and a lighter peripheral part. When L-strains grow under poor, crowded conditions, the similarities of their colonies with those of PPLO can become so great that even the expert may be misled. In liquid the difference is greater, for PPLO grow either with a faint turbidity or as small granules, whereas L-cultures grow in large clumps or flakes or, as in the case of Proteus L-form, with a strong turbidity and a thick veil.

With regard to the colonies produced by PPLO and L-forms of bacteria on solid agar medium, Razin and Oliver (1961) point out that this is due to the small size of their cells and their lack of rigid cell walls. From their investigation on the morphogenesis of the colonies of both groups, these authors drew the conclusion that the inoculated cells are drawn into the agar gel together with the water surrounding them. Consequently the multiplication of these cells starts inside the agar where they produce a ball-like colony in contrast to bacteria which produce wedge-shaped colonies in pour plates. The authors point out ". . . the forces responsible for drawing the microorganisms into the agar are the capillary forces of the agar gel. The determinant factors of the actual penetration, however, are the very small dimensions and the plastic nature of the *Mycoplasma* and L-form causing these organisms to enter between the agar fibrils and to move in the interstices of the fibrillar network of the agar gel." When the growing organisms reach the agar surface the growth spreads into the thin water film which covers the agar and then the peripheral zone is formed. The authors have further shown that most of the viable small particles of PPLO sown on to the surface penetrate the agar, whereas only a fraction of the L-form cells are drawn into it. These differences may be explained by the fact that fewer cells of very small dimensions occur in the L-forms than in the PPLO. When the agar is very soft and moist, the penetration does not take place and surface colonies without central parts develop. Razin and Oliver's studies show that the similarity of PPLO and L-form colonies is due to physical forces and the smallness and plasticity of the organisms, and not to some intrinsic genetical relationship between the two groups.

With regard to morphology, the elements of both kinds of cultures can be very pleomorphic on solid media, a property no doubt due to their lack of a solid cell wall. However, there are important differences. The smallest particles of PPLO (minimal reproductive units) measure, as has been mentioned before, about 125 m$\mu$ in diameter; they occur in large number as a uniform phase and are regularly arranged in their mother cells. In the L-form the diameter of the smallest particles seems to measure about 200–300 m$\mu$; they are not uniform in size and appear to be less numerous and not so regularly arranged (see Fig. 37). The difference in the size of the smallest particles has been demonstrated by filtration experiments and electron microscopy. So far only a few organisms have been thoroughly examined in each group. If these studies were extended the differences could probably be established more conclusively. The further development of the smallest elements in the two groups shows an even greater discrepancy. As pointed out in the chapter on morphology, the PPLO granules swell and grow in liquid media into small PPLO-cells which may be round, oval, hour-glass shaped or filamentous. On solid media they often grow into large flat PPLO-cells of various shapes. These cells differentiate into concentrated and thin parts and the concentrated parts often occur as outer ridges; they produce the minimal reproductive units. In the L-forms the granules that grow up into dense easily stainable elements seem to lie within a delicately staining matrix. As seen from Figs. 34, 35 and 36, this matrix spreads out from the bigger elements and seems to cover the field of vision as a delicate slime. The conjecture that this matrix is necessary for the development of the granules may perhaps be permitted, as it explains a number of recent observations.

Roux (1960), for example, concludes from recent studies that the small granules occurring in L-form are not viable. He applied micromanipulation to the various elements of a stable L-form derived from *Proteus vulgaris*. He found that one out of two of the larger cells was viable after micromanipulation and was able to produce progeny.

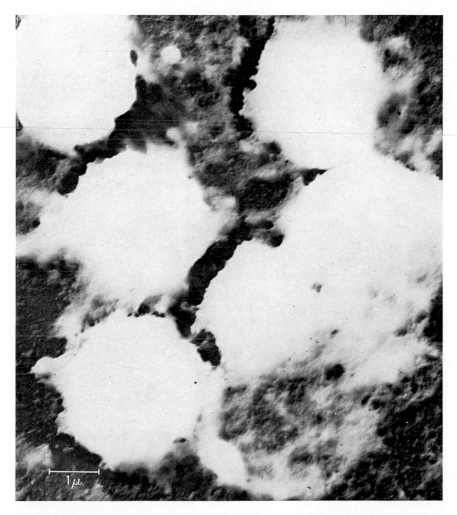

FIG. 34. Electron micrograph of stable L-form of *Streptobacillus moniliformis*. The organism was grown in liquid medium and shaken during growth. The sediment was washed twice and resuspended in Tyrode–Ringer solution. Drops of this suspension served as inoculum for a Formvar film covering solid medium which was incubated at 37°C for 18 hours. The membrane culture was treated and electron-micrographed as described. Note the matrix substance in which the big cells and the granules are lying.

However, none of the granular forms yielded growth after this operation. If the supposition that the granules must be surrounded by their delicate matrix in order to develop is correct, it would explain Roux's failure to grow them after micromanipulation.

The short publications by Thorsson and Weibull (1958) and Weibull

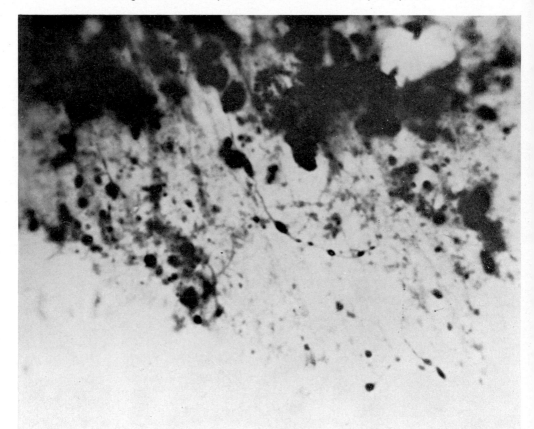

Fig. 35. Growing edge of a young colony (18 hours) of a stable L-form of *Proteus vulgaris* "L9". Agar fixation-Giemsa method. Note the fine granules and the delicately and irregularly distributed matrix substance and also the filamentous strands containing small elements. Magnification: × 1200.

and Beckman (1960b), throw some new light on the possible nature of the small granules in L-forms. In the first communication the authors show an ultra-thin section of small corpuscles surrounded by an "envelope". The authors are of the opinion that the particles are "well-defined structural elements and not merely protoplasmic fragments". In the second study, Weibull and Beckman were concerned with the metabolism of the small bodies isolated from a stable Proteus L-form. They separated the small bodies measuring 0·1 to 0·3 μ from the rest of the culture by differential centrifugation. It was found that the respiration of the small bodies is of the same order of magnitude as that of the whole L-culture. However, the biosynthetic capabilities of the L-granules were found to be very low compared with unfractionated L-cultures. Their respiratory activity shows that the granules are alive; perhaps they need their matrix in order to unfold their biosynthetic capabilities.

Biochemical studies of a similar kind were carried out by Mandel *et al.* (1959). They also used differential centrifugation and produced 4 fractions of different average sizes from a stable Proteus L-form. They recorded that the fraction containing the smallest granules which also had passed a 3 L3 Chamberland filter, was of very low enzymatic activity but contained a high percentage of deoxyribonucleic acid and the lowest of ribonucleic acid.

Panos *et al.* (1960) applied ultrasonic treatment and filtration to the L-form of a streptococcus and thus released and recovered granular elements of an average size of 300 mμ which they considered capable of reproducing the L-growth.

There are many other differences which taken together are quite impressive. First of all another more or less morphological distinction. Growth and individual cells are much more delicate in PPLO than in L-forms. PPLO cells have less substance and therefore take stain less readily than L-cells, many of which stain quickly and deeply. However, the faint matrix substance seen in L-cultures (compare illustrations) is not present in PPLO growth. The electron microscope, it is hoped, will reveal more structural differences between L-forms and PPLO which cannot be resolved by the light microscope. Ultrathin sections, though often difficult to interpret, should contribute vital information (see Edwards and Fogh, 1960). It seems necessary that the exploration of the morphology by means of ultrathin sections be preceded by thorough studies of unsectioned organisms and that the influence of various techniques of fixation and embedding should be properly examined (see Giesbrecht, 1960). New and valuable information can hardly be expected otherwise.

At the present stage of our knowledge, non-morphological evidence for the distinction of the two groups may seem more convincing to many bacteriologists. For example: PPLO are widely distributed in nature, some are saprophytic but many more are parasitic, pathogenic organisms. In contrast, stable L-forms are exclusively a laboratory product. So far stable L-forms have never been cultured from diseased animals or humans, though swollen bacteria have been observed. L-forms from pathogenic organisms are, as a rule, non-pathogenic.

A number of the PPLO species are very exacting with regard to their nutritive requirements, and though there are exceptions among them, many of them grow on the same media and probably have similar

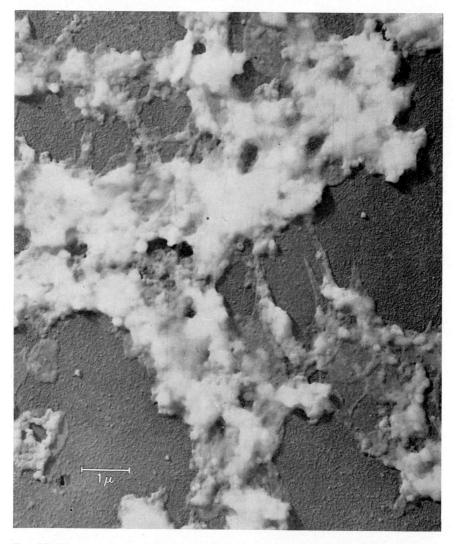

FIG. 36. Electron micrograph of stable L-form of *Proteus vulgaris* "L9." The organism was grown in liquid medium and shaken during growth. The sediment was washed twice and resuspended in Tyrode-Ringer solution. Drops of this suspension served as inoculum for a Formvar film covering solid medium which was incubated at 37°C for two hours and then kept at 4°C over-night. The membrane culture was treated and electron-micrographed as described. Note the granules of various sizes embedded in a matrix substance.

metabolic activities. They grow in the first instance as well as they do later unless they have been under adverse conditions prior to isolation. In contrast, L-forms are often very difficult to produce, they show great fragility at first and many passages at short intervals may be necessary to obtain a well growing non-reverting stable L-strain. When established, stable L-strains are easy to grow and not exacting. No definite method can be outlined that will lead to the successful production of an L-culture proper and two bacterial strains of the same species may differ when attempts are made to transform them into the L-form.

Edward (1953) showed that PPLO need cholesterol, whereas L-

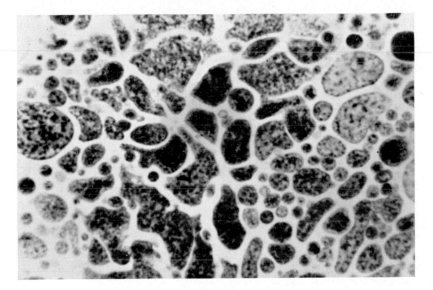

Fig. 37. Stable L-form of a gram-negative anaerobic bacterium isolated from an abscess in a rabbit's ear. Agar fixation-Giemsa method. Magnification: × 1200. Note the cells containing irregularly distributed granules.

forms can dispense with that substance. The L-forms differ widely in their metabolic activities from each other and follow in this respect the parent cultures from which they are derived. Kandler *et al.* (1956) and Zehender (1956) studied the oxidative metabolism of *Proteus vulgaris*, its stable L-form, and some PPLO. They added carbohydrates, organic acids, amino acids and alcohols to suspensions of organisms and found that PPLO, in contrast to bacteria and L-forms, are not able to break down organic acids and amino acids. The reaction of PPLO to substances which poison oxidation systems is of great interest. The above-mentioned authors found that PPLO are sensitive to monoiodoacetic acid and fluoride and completely resistant to potassium cyanide and

dinitrophenol; they are further resistant to azide, arsenite and arse-
nate. Therefore the conclusion must be drawn that PPLO are neither
dependent on the cytochrome system nor on the citric acid cycle. The
sensitivity of the PPLO to monoiodoacetic acid and fluoride suggests
that they follow the Embden-Meyerhof scheme up to the production
of pyruvic acid in their degradative activities. On the basis of these
results the authors consider the PPLO to be an independent class of
organisms and not stable L-forms of bacteria.

Most species of PPLO are serologically distinct, although they do
possess some slight antigenic relationships. Only closely related organisms such as the one causing pleuropneumonia in cattle and that
causing a similar disease in goats, have a marked antigenic relationship. The antigenic structure of an L-strain is always similar to that of
the parent culture apart from the antigens associated with the cell wall.

The study of bacterial protoplasts suggests that a relationship may
exist between the L-forms and these cellular elements which have been
deprived of their cell walls by the action of lysozyme. Although the
lysozyme-produced protoplasts can assimilate and increase their substance, they cannot reproduce themselves upon transfer. According to
Weibull (1958), the difference between L-form and lysozyme-produced
protoplasts may be that the L-form still has a minimal amount of some
cell wall substances, whereas protoplasts have none. I expect that in
the near future the chemists will find out in what special property
protoplasts and L-forms differ.

The so-called "protoplasts" (spheroplasts) described by Lederberg
and St. Clair (1958) have been obtained by the action of penicillin on
bacteria in the same way as "transition forms" or "unstable L-forms"
have been produced by many workers in the past. Lederberg and St.
Clair's growth form reverts just as transition forms do when the penicillin is omitted from the medium or destroyed by penicillinase. They
should therefore not be called protoplasts but "transition forms" or
"unstable L-forms" or "spheroplasts" (Brenner et al. 1958).

## C.   On the Hypothesis of Transformations

The hypothesis that bacteria proper can transform into PPLO via
the L-form and that PPLO—again via the L-form—can revert into
bacteria, falls into line with conceptions which seem to have haunted
the minds of bacteriologists periodically (Wittler et al. 1956; Smith et
al. 1957; Minck, 1955; Kelton et al. 1960; Ruys, 1960; van Iterson and
Ruys, 1960a and b). Thirty years ago transformations of gram-positive
cocci into gram-negative rods and of gram-negative bacilli (B. coli)
into enterococci were very topical (Schmidt-Kehl, 1930; Kuhn, 1929).
These "results" had been obtained by means of an elaborate technique

including micromanipulations. However, they are completely forgotten today. In the recent literature similar claims have been voiced, but they have also been critically appraised (Paine and Daniel 1959; Briggs *et al.* 1959; Hilson and Elek, 1959). At the International meeting on "The Biology of Pleuropneumonia-like Organisms" held in January 1959, under the auspices of the New York Academy of Science, there was a considerable body of opinion in favour of the idea of transformation of bacteria into PPLO and vice versa. The onus of the proof is, of course, on those who have claimed that their researches led to such conclusions. It is up to the rest of us to examine critically the methods that seem to have produced evidence for such far-reaching conclusions which, in view of the dissimilarities between PPLO and L-form pointed out above, seem unlikely. In many cases it will be found that sufficient and adequate controls have not been included in the studies and that loop-holes, however small, have been left open for contaminants to slip in. Also it is often not realized that apparently pure cultures may contain a second organism in small amounts or in an inhibited state. Under certain conditions, unknown to us, this second organism may flare up and then appear unexpectedly. It is by no means an easy task to make sure that a culture is pure and it is similarly difficult to exclude all possibilities of contamination. PPLO have been cultured from strains of gonococci, from *Fusiformis necrophorus*, from *Trichomonas vaginalis* and from various strains of tissue cultures. All these cultures were regarded as pure cultures before the admixture was discovered.

When only thoroughly autoclaved media are used for growing cultures, the task of procuring pure cultures and keeping them pure, is difficult enough. Any non-autoclaved materials such as blood, serum, bits of organs, etc., added to the medium, contribute a factor of uncertainty and may endanger the issue. However, when animal passages, or tissue cultures or embryonated eggs are introduced into the procedures at one stage or another, the possibility of picking up an agent latent in the animal or carried in the tissue cultures or eggs constitutes an even greater danger. As a study of the literature will show, it is not only beginners or the inexperienced, but also wise and experienced workers who have been trapped in these snares (Wilson, 1959).

It may be instructive to comment on a few of the recent reports dealing with "transformations".

The experiments can be divided into two categories, those in which tissue culture or embryonated eggs have been used for growing the hypothetical bacteria, and those in which media only were used. The workers who have used eggs or tissues to pass on the PPLO have apparently not fully realized that both may contain microbes. The egg culture in particular may contain chicken pathogens which are passed on from one generation of birds to the other by means of the eggs, for example coccobacilliform bodies and *Haemophilus gallinarum*. "Controls" may be very misleading because a single egg containing an organism may suffice to produce a positive result in the experimental series although all the controls may be negative. Further, there is the possibility of lighting up the latent coccobacilliform bodies or the *Haemophilus gallinarum* by means of the inoculum. This may have happened in the experiments of McKay and Truscott (1960) who inoculated coccobacilliform bodies into eggs from which they isolated *Haemophilus gallinarum*. The presence of a latent organism is often not discovered until it is induced to multiply by a stimulus. The present author is here in perfect agreement with Nelson who likened the employment of contaminated tissue culture to the use of naturally infected animals. In both instances, he said, "the observed response to an introduced agent might be abnormal and might lead to false conclusions" (report of discussion, Part II, "Biology of the PPLO", 1960). It is well known, and it has been mentioned in this book, that the introduction of a virus or even of sterile material into the brains of mice may "light up" a PPLO otherwise not demonstrable. Thus animals, tissue culture and embryonated eggs must be excluded from experiments devised to demonstrate the transformation of one living agent into another.

Let us turn to experimental work in which sterilized media were used. One of the best papers in this class that seems superficially to carry some conviction, until properly analysed, is that by Smith *et al*. (1957). In Table 1 of their paper it is shown how often diphtheroids turned up in broth tubes inoculated with a certain strain of PPLO. One hundred tubes were used in the experiment; agar blocks were cut out from a plate covered with colonies of PPLO and these served as inoculum. In the controls, blocks of sterile agar were used for inoculation. However, it must be realized that the plate which grew the PPLO had been opened and streaked by means of an agar block from another plate similarly treated and so on. Thus the experimental series was more exposed to accidental contamination than the control series. Although the plates were examined before the cutting out of the blocks, tiny groups of diphtheroids could easily have escaped low power microscopical examination, and some diphtheroids grow very reluctantly and very slowly. The controls are therefore quite inadequate and one would *a priori*, expect fewer contaminants in the control series than in the experimental one. A similar objection can be raised with respect to the second experiment, where in the experimental series broth tubes were inoculated from broth tubes which had previously been opened for subculture, whereas the control tubes had been inoculated from sterile broth tubes. However, manipulations carried out with tubes are less dangerous with regard to contaminations than those carried out with plates; this is borne out by the fact that in the agar-block broth experiments diphtheroids were found 18 times in 100 tubes, whereas in the broth-broth-tube experiments they were encountered 5 times in 100 tubes. These experiments show how unsuitable ordinary bacteriological techniques are for the demonstration of transformations. This has been previously demonstrated by Klieneberger in 1932.

The controls set up are inadequate for another reason also. A diphtheroid falling into a sterile tube may not grow out by itself; however, two different organisms together in a tube of nutrient medium create conditions quite different to those produced by one organism alone. There may be synergism or antagonism when two living entities are simultaneously present in media, in cell cultures or in animals. So far the factors responsible for these phenomena have hardly been explored. Therefore the outcome of experiments such as those discussed here cannot be accepted as proof of the claims that PPLO transform into bacteria.

### D.   The Deceptive Appearance of Colonies

Another fact that might lead to a wrong conclusion when dealing with a differentiation between L-forms of bacteria and PPLO should here be mentioned: namely, the appearance of PPLO colonies which have developed under adverse conditions. When a bacterium or a PPLO is first isolated it is not always in a healthy state. The following experiment may illustrate this. A *Streptobacillus moniliformis* culture isolated from a diseased animal produces unstable L-form spontaneously in suitable media, probably due to the adverse conditions it was exposed to in the animal. I transferred such a culture every day, each time allowing it to grow for six hours only; it was then placed in the cold to be subcultured again the next day and so forth. The culture changed very gradually until after two years it had the appearance of an ordinary gram-negative streptobacillus; it did not produce swollen forms until 48 hours had elapsed or penicillin was used for induction. This shows that an organism when propagated for a long period under favourable conditions loses its tendency to pleomorphism and L-form production and its colonies may also have a different appearance. In the case of the *Streptobacillus moniliformis*, the freshly isolated culture produced a large amount of myelin structures which appeared as "holes" under low magnification (Partridge and Klieneberger, 1941), whereas the culture which had been repeatedly transferred showed no "holes".

When PPLO have grown under adverse conditions, for example either in the presence of their antiserum or together with some other organisms, such as for example *Trichomonas vaginalis* or in tissue culture, they often produce colonies which contain a large number of enormous PPLO-cells. The type of growth produced is well illustrated in the paper by Peoples *et al.* (1957) in their Fig. 2, page 400; they describe the colony as lacy and vacuolated. Figure 38 shows a young colony of a human PPLO grown in the presence of its antiserum with a similar appearance due to the presence of large PPLO-cells. Strains which are found to be in this condition usually require a considerable number of transfers in order to grow normally. They seem to simulate L-form in their appearance. However, their finer structure as seen after the application of the agar-fixation-Giemsa technique is typical and the cells

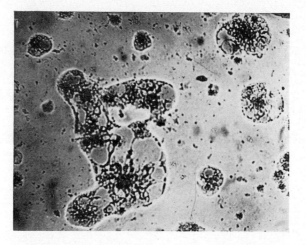

Fig. 38.   Colonies of a human genital PPLO strain grown 3 days under the influence of homologous antiserum. Magnification:  × 54.

are clearly shown to contain the minimal reproductive units which, at a later date, develop into small cells filling out the mother cells. The appearance of colonies similar to those described here may be misleading, but a study of the fine structure will always enable one to diagnose the colonies correctly.

## E.   Tissue Culture Contaminants

Recent reports on the occurrence of PPLO and L-forms in tissue culture make another digression necessary.

It is feasible that L-form can develop from bacteria in tissue culture under the influence of penicillin often used to suppress bacteria. Yet stable L-form has not been encountered in tissue culture so far. Holmgren and Campbell (1960) reported the occurrence in a tissue culture line of an unstable L-form which reverted to the bacterial form after elimination of the antibiotics.

However, many tissue cultures have been reported to be contaminated with PPLO (Robinson et al. (1956), Collier (1957), Rothblatt and Morton (1958), Hearn et al. (1959), Hayflick (1960)). It is difficult to know why so many cell lines are contaminated with these organisms. Some authors think that their small colonies from tissue culture are L-forms derived from bacteria (see Macpherson and Allner, 1960), but all the cell lines that we have investigated contained genuine PPLO and not L-forms. As no convincing evidence has been forthcoming so far to prove that stable L-form and PPLO are identical, nor that bacteria transform into PPLO or the other way round, other sources for the PPLO in tissue cultures have to be considered. My guess is that some cell lines may have been contaminated in the first place because the organ from which they were derived was infected with PPLO. The other tissue cultures may have been cross-contaminated from these, as admittedly the methods used in virus departments do not always conform to strict requirements of asepsis. An indication of the possibility of cross-infection is provided by the fact that Lemcke (unpublished) found in my laboratory that three different cell lines, namely HeLa cells, an embryo rabbit kidney and a monkey kidney line, were contaminated with the same type of organism, a human genital PPLO strain.

For all the reasons discussed we must distinguish between bacteria, their L-forms, and PPLO as different entities so long as those who promote the ideas of transformation have not conclusively proven that the claimed transformations occur regularly in their own and other hands by methods which stand up to criticism. It should be emphasized here again that PPLO and L-forms are different in many respects and that in well-stained preparations they can always be distinguished from each other by the different appearance of their granular matter. As seen in Figs. 16a, b and 37, PPLO show up their minimal reproductive units as darkly stained, uniform elements, lying singly and in a regular pattern, whereas in L-forms the granular matter is irregularly arranged, often less deeply stained and does not give the impression of a uniform phase of cells.

# CHAPTER VIII

# Nutrition and Metabolism of Pleuropneumonia-like Organisms

## BY S. RAZIN

The nutrition and metabolism of PPLO are of special interest, as they are the smallest organisms capable of growing in cell-free media. The small dimensions of the PPLO limit the number of protein molecules and enzymes contained within their cells, thereby explaining their poor catabolic activity and biosynthetic powers. As a result of this limited and sluggish metabolic activity, the rate of growth of the PPLO is slow and the yields of organism from cultures are low. Nutritional studies are therefore complicated by the difficulty in the assessment of the amount of growth of these organisms (Smith, 1956; Butler and Knight, 1960a). Metabolic studies of the PPLO have likewise been impeded by the difficulties encountered in growing large quantities of PPLO and obtaining active washed suspensions (Pirie and Holmes, 1933; Smith and Sasaki, 1958; Neimark and Pickett, 1960; Butler and Knight, 1960b).

The culture media at present available are also not yet entirely satisfactory, and most workers agree that more PPLO strains are likely to be discovered with the improvement of present media. Large strides towards a better understanding of the nutrition and metabolism of the PPLO have been made during the last decade. Despite this development, no chemically-defined medium has so far been devised even for the least exacting PPLO strains. Our knowledge about the nutritional requirements of PPLO is based on experiments performed with partially defined media and a restricted number of strains. The conclusions drawn from these experiments are therefore always open to criticism especially if sweeping generalizations are drawn from them.

## A. CHEMICAL COMPOSITION OF PPLO

Information about the chemical composition of the PPLO is very scanty. The few studies carried out were concerned with certain cell constituents only, and a complete chemical analysis of any of the PPLO strains is not available. The findings of Kandler (1956) and of Lynn and Smith (1957, 1960) do not reveal any essential difference in chemical composition between the PPLO strains tested and bacteria, except for a lower nucleic acid content and the presence of cholesterol in PPLO. Trace amounts of sterols have been found only in very few bacterial species up till now (Fiertel and Klein, 1959).

A galactan comprising about 10% of the dry weight of the bovine pleuropneumonia organism was described by Plackett and Buttery (1958). Diaminopimelic acid and hexosamines, known to be constituents of the "mucopeptide complex" responsible for the rigidity of bacterial cell walls, do not seem to be present in the plastic PPLO-cells (Kandler and Zehender, 1957; Plackett, 1959).

## B.  Growth Factors and their Metabolism

### 1. *Lipids*

#### (a) *Cholesterol Requirement*

Lipids play a role of prime importance in the nutrition and metabolism of PPLO. Edward and Fitzgerald (1951b) and others (Smith *et al.* 1954; Smith and Lynn, 1958; Rodwell, 1956; Freundt, 1958), have shown cholesterol to be essential for the growth of the parasitic PPLO in serum-free media. Some protozoa (van Wagtendonk, 1955) and the larval and pupal stages of several insects (Beck and Kapadia, 1957) also require cholesterol for growth. A nutritional requirement for cholesterol is unknown as yet for any other group of bacteria.

The uptake of cholesterol by PPLO cells during growth has been demonstrated (Smith, 1960a). The amounts of cholesterol required for optimal growth depend on the concentration of other constituents of the culture medium and vary between 0·004 and 0·5 mg. cholesterol per ml. medium (Edward and Fitzgerald, 1951b; Smith and Lynn, 1958; Freundt, 1958; Rodwell, 1960a; Butler and Knight, 1960c), the average being 0·01–0·05 mg./ml. Hence the amounts of cholesterol required for growth of PPLO are significantly higher than those of vitamins required for growth of other microorganisms. However, it should be taken into consideration that free cholesterol does not dissolve in aqueous solutions but forms emulsions. Therefore the real concentration of soluble cholesterol in the medium is unknown.

The saprophytic PPLO strains apparently do not need cholesterol for growth, since these strains could be grown on a medium rendered lipid-free by ether extraction (Smith, 1960a), and on a cholesterol free partially defined medium (Razin and Knight, 1960a). These observations may be correlated with the fact that no cholesterol could be detected in the saprophytic PPLO, whereas significant amounts were found in parasitic PPLO (Lynn and Smith, 1960). The observation of Butler and Knight (1960c) that some growth of the saprophytic PPLO in a peptone yeast extract medium could be obtained by the addition of cholesterol, or some of its analogues, might be explained by its detoxifying properties, e.g. against traces of fatty acids present in the medium (Pollock, 1949). Crystallized bovine plasma albumin, a known fatty-acid detoxifier (Davies and Dubos, 1947), produced even better growth than cholesterol when added to the peptone yeast extract medium (Butler and Knight, 1960c).

Cholesterol may be replaced by several closely related sterols, such as cholestanol, stigmasterol, beta-sitosterol, ergosterol and epicholesterol (Edward and Fitzgerald, 1951b; Smith and Lynn, 1958). Various PPLO which contain cholesterol esterase are able to utilize certain cholesteryl esters instead of cholesterol (Smith and Lynn, 1958; Smith, 1959). Removal of the side chain, aromatization of ring A, oxidation of the 3-OH to a keto group, reduction of the hydrocarbon, or formation of an ether linkage at the 3-OH group of cholesterol, completely abolished the growth-promoting activity of cholesterol (Smith and Lynn, 1958; Smith, 1960a). Butler and Knight (1960c), however, found that replacement of the 3-OH group by a keto group did not affect the low growth-promoting activity of cholesterol towards the saprophytic PPLO in a peptone yeast extract medium.

Several steroids were found to inhibit growth of PPLO (Smith and Lynn, 1958; Smith, 1960a; Butler and Knight, 1960c). This could be overcome by raising the concentration of cholesterol in the medium (Butler and Knight, 1960c). The nature of growth inhibition by steroids will probably remain obscure until the elucidation of the mechanism of growth promotion by cholesterol.

Possible mechanisms for cholesterol activity were discussed in detail by Smith (1960a). Accordingly, cholesterol might fulfil one or more of the following functions.

*Detoxification of Fatty Acids.* Cholesterol might bind fatty acids by ester formation and slowly release them in the required non-toxic amounts. A lytic effect of oleic and other unsaturated fatty acids on PPLO has been observed (Edward and Fitzgerald, 1951b; Rodwell, 1956). Rodwell (1956) showed that cholesterol could neutralize this lytic effect. Smith (1960a), however, was unable to decrease the inhibitory action of fatty acids by cholesterol, and concluded that cholesterol does not act as a detoxifier. But even if it did, this would certainly not be its only function, because other fatty-acid detoxifiers, such as bovine albumin (Davies and Dubos, 1947) and starch (Ley and Mueller, 1946), cannot replace the cholesterol requirement of parasitic PPLO (Edward and Fitzgerald, 1951b; Rodwell, 1956; Smith, 1960a).

*Provision of an Oxidizable Substrate.* The possibility that cholesterol might serve as a carbon and energy source for PPLO was tested by Smith (1960a). The experiments did not show any degradation of cholesterol, either by growing or by resting organisms. Conner (1957) and Talalay, *et al.* (1958) suggested that steroids might function as cofactors of oxidative phosphorylation systems. No evidence for such a function of cholesterol in PPLO was found by Smith (1960a).

*Maintenance of the Structural Integrity of the Organisms.* Cholesterol may serve as a component of the lipoproteins of mitochondria and cell membrane, and thus aid in solubilization of water-insoluble lipids (Smith, 1960a). Cholesterol was found in the cell debris of PPLO, indicating its presence in the cell membrane (Lynn and Smith, 1960).

*Participation in the Permeation of Substrates into the Cells.* Essential fatty acids might gain entrance to the cell by forming esters with the cholesterol present in the cell membrane by the mediation of cholesterol esterase. The cholesteryl esters might then be transported across the cell membrane and hydrolyzed to liberate free fatty acids or acyl coenzyme A as an oxidizable substrate (Smith, 1960a). Short-chain fatty acids stimulate the growth of several PPLO strains (Smith and Lynn, 1958; Lynn, 1960). However, most PPLO strains are not dependent on fatty acids for growth.

## (b) *Phospholipid Requirement*

Edward and Fitzgerald (1951b) noted that in addition to cholesterol and bovine albumin, an acetone-insoluble lipid fraction of egg yolk was essential for optimal growth of certain strains of PPLO in a serumless medium. Attempts to identify the growth factor present in this fraction were unsuccessful (Edward, 1954). Lecithin was shown by Smith, Lecce and Lynn (1954) to promote growth of PPLO in serumfree media. The requirement for lecithin, however, was not specific, as this could be replaced by sodium cholate (Smith and Lynn, 1958). Smith (1960a) gave the opinion that lecithin and cholate, which are surface-active substances, promote growth by increasing the solubility of cholesterol, making it more available to the organisms. Neither lecithin nor cholate were included in the partially defined medium for the bovine pleuropneumonia organism devised by Rodwell (1960a). The solubilization of cholesterol could be carried out in this case by Tween 80, present in the medium (Rodwell, 1960b). Lecithin was not required by certain saprophytic PPLO (Razin and Knight, 1960a).

## (c) *Fatty Acid Requirements*

A growth requirement for oleic acid was described by Rodwell (1956) who used the bovine strain of pleuropneumonia as a test organism. Oleic acid could be replaced by linoleic, linolenic acid or Tween 80. The amount of fatty acid required for optimal growth was related to the amounts of cholesterol and serum protein fraction present in the medium. Rodwell (1956) suggested that cholesterol and serum protein bind the toxic fatty acid and release it in small non-toxic amounts sufficient for growth. Smith (1960a) and Razin and Knight (1960a) could not demonstrate any requirement for unsaturated fatty acids, using different PPLO strains and media. In view of these negative results, Rodwell (1960b) advanced the hypothesis that there is no specific fatty acid requirement and that the sodium oleate or Tween 80, included in his medium, simply act as surface-depressing agents solubilizing cholesterol.

## (d) Glycerol Requirement

Glycerol was shown to be necessary for the growth of the bovine pleuropneumonia organism (Rodwell, 1960a). Radioactively labelled glycerol was found to be incorporated into cell lipids and into a fraction chemically resembling the glycerophosphoprotein complex of staphylococcal cell membranes (Rodwell, 1960a; Mitchell and Moyle, 1951).

## (e) Cholesterol Esterase

PPLO strains able to utilize cholesteryl esters for growth were found to possess cholesterol esterase activity (Smith, 1959; Smith, 1960a). No co-factor was required for this reaction. Lecithin and other surface active substances (cholate, cephalin, soap) enhanced enzymic activity, apparently by solubilizing the sterol. Optimal activity of the esterase was at pH 6.5, which is significantly lower than the optimal pH value for growth. A slight synthesis of cholesteryl esters from free cholesterol and fatty acids occurred with whole organisms. This reaction was much slower than the hydrolysis. Coenzyme A and ATP were necessary co-factors for the synthetic reaction, and stimulated the hydrolytic reaction. The fatty acids are apparently activated to form acyl-coenzyme A. The esterase activity of ultrasonically broken organisms was found in the cellular residue (? cell membrane) and not in the supernatant fluid (cell protoplasm). The growth inhibitory steroids (Smith and Lynn, 1958) cholestane and bicholesteryl ether, also inhibit cholesterol esterase activity.

## (f) Lipases

The formation of a "pearly" film and small spots by certain PPLO strains in serum media was described by Edward (1950, 1954). The spots were found to consist of calcium and magnesium soaps. The composition of the "pearly" film seems to be more complex; cholesterol and phospholipids have been detected in it. The film and spots are apparently the result of the lipase and cholesterol esterase activities that have been demonstrated in various PPLO strains (Smith, 1959, 1960a).

## (g) *Oxidation of Fatty Acids*

The oxidation of short-chain fatty acids by several PPLO strains was reported by Lynn (1960). The fatty acids oxidized included acetate, propionate, butyrate, caprylate and valerate. These findings support the view expressed by Smith (1960a) that short-chain fatty acids serve as the main carbon and energy source for human PPLO strains which cannot utilize carbohydrates.

## 2. *Proteins and Amino Acids*

### (a) *Lipoprotein Requirement*

As a first step towards the development of a chemically defined medium for PPLO, attempts were made by several workers to replace the serum component of complex media by known substances. The results obtained so far suggest that the active factor of the serum is a complex of protein–cholesterol–phospholipid (Edward and Fitzgerald, 1951b; Smith, *et al.* 1954; Rodwell, 1956).

Smith and Morton (1951b, 1952), Smith *et al.* (1954) isolated and purified active protein material from bovine serum. The protein was classified as an alpha-1-lipoprotein. It was also found in other mammalian sera and is probably present in haemoglobin, yeasts, and bacteria (Smith and Morton, 1951b). This protein had a low molecular weight, and could be precipitated by complete saturation with ammonium sulphate and was stable to heat; it was basic in nature and contained a restricted number of amino acids. The serum protein fractions prepared by Priestley and White (1952) and by Rodwell (1956), apparently contained this active lipoprotein.

The requirement for lipoprotein was only partially specific. This could be replaced to a limited extent by serum albumin and beta-lactoglobulin (Smith, 1960a). On a quantitative basis, these two proteins were only one tenth as active as the lipoprotein. The differences in the growth-promoting activities of the various proteins were correlated with their capacity to bind cholesterol. The active lipoprotein could bind approximately four times the amount of cholesterol bound by bovine albumin and beta-lactoglobulin. Proteins inactive in the growth of PPLO failed to bind cholesterol. The lipoprotein could also be partially replaced by soluble starch (Edward and Fitzgerald, 1951; Rodwell, 1956) or charcoal (Smith, 1955a). In addition to the lipoprotein, bovine serum albumin was required for the growth of the bovine pleuropneumonia organism from small inocula in the partially defined medium of Rodwell (1960a); this might be explained by the fact that albumin can bind toxic unsaturated fatty acids (Davies and

Dubos, 1947), whereas the lipoprotein was found to be devoid of this property (Smith, 1960a). The saprophytic PPLO do not seem to require the lipoprotein for growth. Reasonable growth of these strains was obtained in a partially defined medium containing crystallized bovine plasma albumin, instead of serum (Razin and Knight, 1960a).

Degradation of the lipoprotein by chemical and enzymic means abolished its activity completely (Smith, *et al.* 1954; Smith, 1960a). This might be correlated with the finding that various PPLO strains were unable to degrade this protein. The small amounts of the lipoprotein which disappeared from the culture medium during growth, could be accounted for by uptake or adsorption of the intact protein on to the organisms (Smith, 1960a). Analogous results were obtained with tissue cultures (Eagle and Piez, 1960). The serum proteins essential for growth of tissue cells in culture were found not to be degraded by the tissue cells and did not serve as a source of amino acids.

The exact role of the lipoprotein in the growth of PPLO is not yet clear. It seems that the active protein serves primarily as a carrier of essential nutrients, e.g. cholesterol (Smith, 1960a), and in addition it might fulfil the function of a detoxifier (Rodwell, 1956). The possibility that it might be incorporated as a cell lipoprotein cannot yet be ruled out (Smith, 1960a).

## (b) *Amino Acid Requirements*

In the absence of chemically defined media, the analysis of amino acid requirements of the PPLO is very difficult. The information available is therefore scarce and is based on studies carried out with only a few PPLO strains. Smith (1955a, 1960b), working with human strains which cannot utilize carbohydrates, demonstrated a requirement for L-arginine, L-aspartic acid, L-cysteine, L-glutamine, L-glutamic acid, DL-isoleucine, L-methionine, DL-phenylalanine and DL-tryptophan.

Razin and Knight (1960a) used Casamino acids (Difco; acid hydrolyzed) as a source of amino acids in their partially defined medium. The Casamino acids could be partially replaced by known amino acid mixtures.

Rodwell (1960a), working with the bovine pleuropneumonia organism, failed to replace the enzymic casein hydrolyzate present in his partially defined medium by amino acid mixtures; analysis of the amino acid requirements of this organism were therefore impossible.

In spite of the scarcity of information available, it may be concluded that PPLO are quite exacting in their amino acid requirements.

## (c) *Proteinases*

The presence of proteolytic enzymes in PPLO was first indicated by

Longley (1951), who demonstrated the liquefaction of coagulated serum by the goat pleuropneumonia organism, a property also shared by the bovine organism (Freundt, 1958). These two organisms, as well as the saprophytic PPLO, also possess gelatinase activity (Freundt, 1958; Razin and Oliver, 1961).

## (d)  *Breakdown of Amino Acids*

The only extensive study of amino acid metabolism by PPLO was carried out by Smith (1955b, 1957a, b, c, 1960b). This study was limited to human strains, which are unable to utilize carbohydrates. The following amino acids were found to be metabolized: tyrosine, tryptophan, aspartic acid, histidine, leucine, threonine, arginine, glutamic acid, glutamine. Some of the metabolized amino acids were deaminated, whereas none, with the exception of citrulline, was decarboxylated. Transamination reactions which play an important role in the amino acid metabolism of other microorganisms, could not be demonstrated in the PPLO strains tested (Smith, 1955b).

The fate of some of the metabolized amino acids was studied by Smith. Glutamine was found to undergo a phosphorolytic deamidation, yielding high energy phosphate bonds (Smith, 1957a). The glutamic acid formed from glutamine was found to undergo a series of reactions leading to the formation of proline. The function of glutamic acid in the human PPLO strains seems to be solely anabolic, as it was not deaminated or decarboxylated by the organisms (Smith, 1957b). Nothing definite is known as yet about the fate of aspartic acid. Deamination accounts for less than 25% of the aspartic acid utilized (Somerson, 1954; Smith, 1960b). The absolute requirement for this acid (Smith, 1955a) indicates its use for anabolic rather than catabolic activity (Smith, 1960b). Arginine is degraded to citrulline by hydrolytic cleavage, which does not supply energy. The citrulline formed undergoes a phosphorolytic cleavage to ornithine, producing high energy phosphate bonds; but the rate of this reaction is very slow and it is doubtful whether it has any significance as an energy source for the organisms (Smith, 1957c).

Smith (1960b) concluded that amino acids do not serve as the sole energy and carbon source for the human PPLO strains tested. These strains might utilize short-chain fatty acids (Lynn, 1960) and monohydric alcohols (Lecce and Morton, 1954) for this purpose. The requirement of a rather small number of amino acids for growth, indicates an extensive synthetic ability. Thus the amino acid metabolism of human PPLO seems predominantly anabolic in nature.

Amino acid catabolism by the organism of bovine pleuropneumonia was studied by Rodwell (1960a). Of the amino acids examined, only serine and threonine were attacked, yielding the corresponding keto acids which were further metabolized. Transaminase activity could not be demonstrated in this organism either.

Some routine biochemical reactions related to amino acid metabolism and employed for differentiation of bacteria were studied by Kandler and Kandler (1955) and Freundt (1958). These authors could not show indole formation and urea degradation by a variety of PPLO strains. Some strains produced traces of $H_2S$ only; thus, these biochemical tests, so practical for the differentiation of bacteria, are of no use when applied to PPLO.

## 3. Carbohydrates

### (a)  Carbohydrate Requirements

Rodwell (1960a) found that glucose or another metabolizable sugar (mannose, fructose) was indispensable for the growth of the bovine pleuropneumonia organism. Labelled glucose added to the medium was shown to be a precursor of the galactan which comprises about 10% of the dry weight of the bovine pleuropneumonia organism. However, only a small fraction of the glucose carbon was incorporated into the galactan; most of the sugar was catabolized and used as an energy source (Plackett, unpublished observations cited by Rodwell, 1960a).

In addition to a metabolizable sugar, high concentrations (0·15M) of sodium L-lactate were required for growth of the bovine pleuropneumonia organism (Rodwell, 1960a). The function of lactate is not yet clear; since very little of it is metabolized, it seems evident that it does not serve simply as an energy source.

Glucose was found to stimulate growth of the saprophytic PPLO in the partially defined medium of Razin and Knight (Razin and Oliver, unpublished observations).

### (b)  Carbohydrate Metabolism

The PPLO may be divided into two groups: one capable of fermenting carbohydrates and the other incapable of doing so (Edward, 1954; Freundt, 1958). The same sugars are usually fermented by the different PPLO species which comprise the given fermentative group. This uniformity limits the use of sugar fermentation tests for the differentiation of PPLO strains (Tourtellotte and Jacobs, 1960). The carbohydrates fermented are: glucose, fructose, mannose, galactose, sucrose, maltose, dextrin, starch, glycogen.

The pathways of carbohydrate metabolism of PPLO were unknown until the last decade. However, evidence for the presence of lactic dehydrogenase in PPLO (Holmes and Pirie, 1932; Pirie and Holmes, 1933; Holmes, 1937; Warren, 1942; Somerson and Morton, 1953; Lecce and Morton, 1954), and for the accumulation of acetic acid as an end product in glucose metabolism by the bovine pleuropneumonia organism (Dujardin-Beaumetz, 1900), was presented much earlier.

The first comprehensive study of carbohydrate metabolism of the

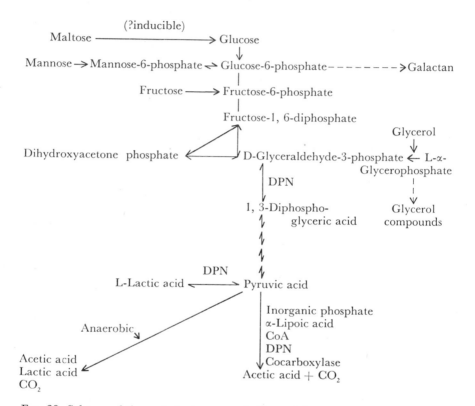

Fig. 39. Scheme of the carbohydrate metabolism of the bovine pleuropneumonia organism. (After Rodwell, 1960a).

bovine pleuropneumonia organism (Fig. 39), was made by Rodwell and Rodwell (1953, 1954a, b, c, Rodwell 1960a).

The results of their study are summarized in the foregoing scheme. The hexoses, glucose, fructose and mannose are degraded through the glycolytic pathway to pyruvate, which is oxidized to acetate and $CO_2$. Coenzyme A, alpha-lipoic acid and diphosphopyridine nucleotide are required for the oxidation of pyruvate. Under anaerobic conditions, pyruvate undergoes dismutation to give lactate, acetate and $CO_2$. The bovine organism was unable to metabolize glucose under anaerobic conditions: this is consistent with the fact that growth of this organism almost failed under anaerobic conditions.

The puzzling problem concerning the absence of glucose degradation under anaerobic conditions, in spite of the presence of the glycolytic system, was dealt with by Rodwell and Rodwell (1954c). They concluded that oxygen is required for the re-oxidation of reduced diphosphopyridine nucleotide (DPN) formed by the oxidation of triose phosphate. In the absence of oxygen, pyruvate is bound by the dismutation system and is not available for reduction to lactate in the glycolysis scheme. The reaction, therefore, ceases when all the DPN has been reduced. The organism possesses no other mechanism for the reoxidation of reduced DPN under anaerobic conditions.

Lactate and glycerol were also oxidized to acetate and $CO_2$ by the bovine organism (Rodwell, 1960a). Lactate was oxidized to pyruvate by a DPN linked lactic dehydrogenase. Glycerol was first phosphorylated and then oxidized by a flavoprotein to glyceraldehyde phosphate which enters the glycolysis cycle. None of the intermediate compounds of the tricarboxylic acid cycle was metabolized by the bovine pleuropneumonia-like organisms. No evidence was found for the presence of the aerobic phosphogluconate pathway in this organism (Rodwell, 1960a).

Rodwell's observations were later extended to almost all other fermentative strains of PPLO by Tourtellotte and Jacobs (1960) and by Neimark and Pickett (1960). Their results usually agree with those of Rodwell, except for Neimark and Pickett's observation that six of the seven strains tested by them were able to metabolize glucose anaerobically. Three of their strains were homofermentative, producing lactate only, while the other four were heterofermentative, producing acetate in addition to lactate. The striking resemblance of the carbohydrate metabolism of these PPLO strains to that of streptococci and lactobacilli, was stressed (Neimark and Pickett, 1960).

On the basis of the evidence obtained so far, it might be concluded that the breakdown of carbohydrates by PPLO is brought about by the glycolytic pathway; the tricarboxylic acid cycle apparently being absent. Hence, the major source of energy in growing cultures is obtained from the breakdown of carbohydrate to the lactate and acetate level. This incomplete and energetically inefficient utilization of carbohydrates might account, at least partially, for the relatively slow growth of PPLO in general.

## (c)  *Terminal Respiratory System*

The terminal respiratory system catalysing the transfer of electrons from reduced DPN to oxygen, was investigated by several authors.

Flavoproteins are probably the enzymes responsible for the electron transfer (Somerson and Morton, 1953), since no evidence for the presence of a cytochrome system in PPLO has been found (Rodwell and Rodwell, 1954a; Zehender, 1956). The requirement for riboflavin shown by PPLO strains (Rodwell, 1960a; Razin and Knight, 1960a) is consistent with this assumption. The presence of catalase in PPLO is still under dispute. Some authors claim that catalase activity may be demonstrated with various PPLO strains (Rodwell and Rodwell, 1954a, Lecce and Morton, 1954), whereas others have not confirmed these findings (Pirie, 1938; Kandler and Kandler, 1955; Freundt, 1958). The high sensitivity of PPLO to hydrogen peroxide (Warren, 1942; Butler and Knight, 1960b) favours the assumption that catalase is either absent from, or present only in very small amounts in, PPLO-cells.

### 4. *Nucleic Acids*

### (a) *Nucleic Acid Precursor Requirements*

The requirement for nucleic acid precursors has been determined only for the few PPLO strains capable of growing in the partially defined media.

Smith (1955a) found RNA and DNA to be essential for growth of some human PPLO strains. Lynn (1956, 1957) tried to replace the RNA and DNA by nucleic acid precursors. Purine and pyrimidine bases, plus ribose and deoxyribose, supported limited growth in a solid (agar) medium only. For growth in a liquid medium, deoxyribosides were needed.

Rodwell (1960a) analyzed the nucleic acid precursor requirements of bovine and goat strains of pleuropneumonia. Guanine, uracil and thymine were required for growth. Omission of adenine decreased growth to about half. Cytosine was not required. The free bases could be replaced by the corresponding nucleosides or nucleotides. No pentose was required.

The partially defined medium of Razin and Knight (1960a) enabled the elucidation of nucleic acid precursor requirements of certain saprophytic PPLO. All strains tested required thymidine (Razin and Knight, 1960b) which could be replaced by folinic acid; folic acid was inactive (Razin, unpublished observations). Thymine was less effective than thymidine in growth promotion. Thymidine seems to play an important role in the biosynthesis of DNA by PPLO. The formation of purine deoxyribosides from purine bases and thymidine by cell extracts of PPLO (Lynn, 1957), supports this assumption.

The effects of undegraded RNA and DNA on the growth of PPLO are of interest. Edward and Fitzgerald (1952) found that the addition of DNA to their complex medium was essential for primary cultures of bovine PPLO. Crowther and Knight (1956), following this observation, found that the DNA was required to overcome a growth inhibition caused by an excess of RNA present in the complex medium. Razin and Knight (1960b) extended these observations and showed that high concentrations of either RNA or DNA inhibited growth of various PPLO strains. This growth inhibition was overcome by raising the concentration of DNA, when RNA was the inhibitor, and visa versa. RNA did not inhibit growth when thymidine replaced the DNA in the growth medium; this led to the assumption that RNA inhibits growth by interfering with the degradation by the organisms of supplied DNA to thymidine, which is a part of DNA, and essential as a nutrient for the growth of the PPLO. The RNA/DNA antagonistic interrelation has also been demonstrated with organisms other than PPLO, namely, *Lactobacillus bifidus* (Skeggs, Spizizen and Wright, 1950) and the L-form of *Streptobacillus moniliformis* (Razin and Knight, 1960b).

## (b) *Nucleic Acid Metabolism*

Nucleic acid metabolism has been but little studied. No information is available about the occurrence of ribonucleases and deoxyribonucleases in PPLO, except for the short report by Plackett (1957), who found ribonuclease activity in cell extracts of the bovine pleuropneumonia organism.

The presence of a deoxyriboside phosphorylase in cell extracts of a human PPLO strain was shown by Lynn (1956, 1957). This enzyme catalyzes the transfer of deoxyribose from thymidine or deoxyinosine to purine bases, giving purine deoxyribosides; inorganic phosphate is required for this reaction.

## 5. *Vitamin Requirements*

Smith (1955a) found that thiamine, pyridoxine, calcium pantothenate, folic acid, biotin and choline were essential nutrients for the growth of some human PPLO strains in his partially defined medium. The bovine pleuropneumonia organism required riboflavin, thiamine and nicotinamide (or nicotinic acid, Rodwell, 1960a), as did the saprophytic "Sewage A" (Razin and Knight, 1960a). Alpha-lipoic acid was not required by the bovine organism when the medium contained bovine serum abulmin fraction V, but growth was decreased by about one half when the more purified crystalline albumin was used instead of fraction V. The goat pleuropneumonia organism exhibited a partial requirement for biotin and pantothenate, in addition to the other vitamins required by the bovine organism (Rodwell, 1960a).

All the results cited above were obtained with partially defined media; therefore they may not represent the exact vitamin requirements of the strains tested. For example, vitamin $B_{12}$, which is usually required in trace amounts, might be supplied by the bovine albumin or lipoprotein present in the medium. The effect of the composition of the medium on the vitamin requirement must also be taken into consideration. Folinic acid becomes essential for the growth of saprophytic PPLO when DNA or thymidine are omitted from the partially defined medium of Razin and Knight (Razin, unpublished observations).

## 6. *Inorganic Ion Requirements*

Inorganic salts constitute an essential part of every culture medium. Ash of Bacto peptone was found to be required by some human PPLO strains grown in the partially defined medium of Smith (1955a). The ash could be replaced, to a large extent, by $Sn^{++}$; other cations were inactive. Apart from supplying essential metal ions, inorganic salts function as buffers and produce a suitable osmotic pressure in the medium. An osmotic pressure of about 12 atm. was required for the growth of the bovine pleuropneumonia organism in the partially defined medium of Rodwell (1956). This was obtained by the incorporation of high concentrations of either sodium acetate, sodium chloride or sucrose in the medium.

The phosphate buffer incorporated into the media of Rodwell (1960a) and Razin and Knight (1960a) prevents a drastic drop in pH value due to acid accumulation during growth. The saprophytic PPLO cannot grow at pH values below 7·0 (Laidlaw and Elford, 1936; Razin and Oliver, 1961).

The only fundamental difference found hitherto between the nutritional requirements of the PPLO and other exacting bacteria is the requirement for the cholesterolli–poprotein–phospholipid complex: this nutritional requirement relates the PPLO to protozoa and the cells of higher organisms. It is only logical to assume that the requirement for this complex is connected in some way with the presence of the peculiar plastic cell membrane of the PPLO. The requirements of the PPLO for amino acids, carbohydrates, nucleic acid precursors and vitamins, and the metabolic pathways involved in their utilization, are essentially similar to those of other nutritionally exacting bacteria, e.g. lactobacilli. However, further elucidation of the nutrition and metabolism of the PPLO might reveal some additional features peculiar to this group of organisms.

# CHAPTER IX

# Susceptibility of Pleuropneumonia-like Organisms to Inhibitory Agents

The results of sensitivity studies with pleuropneumonia-like organisms have been of considerable importance for various reasons. They have facilitated the isolation of PPLO from contaminated material by means of bacteriostatic substances to which PPLO are more or less insensitive; they have given information valuable for the handling of PPLO in experimental work, and they have been instrumental in the discovery of agents suitable for therapeutic purposes.

## A. BACTERIOSTATIC SUBSTANCES

The first bacteriostatic agents to which PPLO were found to be resistant were sulpha drugs. Brown and Hayes in 1942 isolated PPLO from cultures of gonococci with the help of sulphadiazine which was added to the media to supress the gonococci. Gonococci and some other bacteria, for example *Fusiformis necrophorus*, occur together with PPLO on human genitals and it is therefore not surprising that strains of bacteria from these locations develop together with PPLO on artificial media. Beveridge (1943) added sulphanilamide to the media used for the isolation of PPLO from the male urethra. Beveridge, Campbell and Lind (1946), were the first to use penicillin to which PPLO are resistant even in very high concentration; they routinely added 20 units/ml. to their media for the isolation of PPLO. Edward (1947b) investigated the action of a number of bacteriostatic substances on PPLO and on representative bacteria. He found that for practical purposes PPLO were not sufficiently resistant to potassium tellurite, brilliant green and gentian violet to justify their use, whereas, all the diverse PPLO tested grew without any inhibition in a liquid medium containing as much as 1 : 1000 thallium acetate and concentrations of penicillin as high as 390 Oxford units/ml. Penicillin inhibits mainly the non-sporing gram-positive bacteria, whereas thallium acetate is highly bacteriostatic for aerobic spore bearers and gram-negative bacteria. Edward therefore recommended a combination of both in concentrations of 60 units/ml. for penicillin and 1 : 1000 of thallium acetate when "sloppy" agar is used, and 1 : 8000 for a solid agar medium. In my laboratory 50 units/ml. penicillin and thallium acetate in a concentration of 1 : 4000 have consistently and successfully been used for the isolation of PPLO from contaminated material on agar plates. As mentioned before, the PPLO colonies obtained with the help of penicillin should always be transplanted to a penicillin-free medium before the diagnosis "PPLO" is made, in order to avoid confusion with L-forms of bacteria. Edward's results were confirmed by Smith *et al.* (1950) who tested the action on PPLO of a number of substances such as basic fuchsin, brilliant green, crystal violet, nile blue A, potassium tellurite, sodium azide and thionin. Although these substances allowed PPLO to grow, they were not sufficiently inhibitive to bacteria. However, thallium acetate, as reported by Morton and Lecce (1953), has a wide anti-bacterial spectrum; it is not influenced by the protein content of the medium as is, for example, crystal violet and—another advantage—it can be added to the medium before sterilization. Therefore, thallium acetate together with penicillin are the bacteriostatics of choice for the isolation of PPLO from contaminated material.

### B. Sensitivity of PPLO to Agents relatively Innocuous to Bacteria

Although PPLO are resistant to some agents harmful to bacteria, they are very sensitive to some seemingly harmless agents. Most workers found that they die quickly in distilled water and physiological saline and even in broth without serum. Butler and Knight (1960b) in an excellent and revealing study, showed that the survival of washed PPLO depends to a large extent on the quality of the water used for the suspending media. They examined (1) "laboratory distilled water", (2) "glass-distilled water", (3) "deionized water" from a Mark III portable Deminrolit Plant (Permutit Co., Ltd., London, W.4) and (4) "high quality deionized water" (specific conductivity c. $4 \times 10^6$ ohms/cm.) from an Elgastat portable deionizer (type B 102; Elga Products Ltd., London, S.W.19). The survival of washed suspensions was very poor in glass distilled water and also in the following suspending media when made up in glass distilled water: physiological saline, Krebs-Ringer phosphate, potassium phosphate + sucrose (pH 7). The survival of washed PPLO suspensions was greatly improved when certain chelating agents were added. The agents tested were sodium diethyldithiocarbamate, ethylenediamine tetra-acetic acid and 8-hydroxyquinoline; these had to be added in an optimal concentration. The addition of sodium sulphite and of manganese dioxide to phosphate + sucrose in glass distilled water also improved the survival conditions. Even deionized water from a Mark III was not always good enough. However, when high quality deionized water was used for the washing and suspending media, the number of viable particles remained constant during 1 hr. at 2–4°C. It was therefore recommended that when suspensions of PPLO free from the material of culture media are required, the organisms should be washed and suspended in potassium phosphate ($K_2HPO_4$; 0·01M) in high quality deionized water adjusted to pH 7 and held at 2–4°C.

The observation that a temperature of 2–4°C was an optimal survival temperature for organisms suspended in dilute buffer, had already been made by Smith and Sasaki (1958) who, like Butler and Knight, also found that PPLO were relatively insensitive to changes of osmotic pressure. The effectiveness of chelating agents makes it likely that the toxic action of the inferior quality water is due to metal ions.

Butler and Knight are further of the opinion that the toxicity may, in some instances, have been caused by the presence of hydrogen peroxide. This would also explain the great toxicity for PPLO of ascorbic acid which autoxidizes with the formation of hydrogen peroxide. Components of the agar-agar used may also produce hydrogen peroxide on the agar surface. In the experiments of the above authors, lysed red cells abolished the toxic effect of certain agar surfaces, because the catalase contained in the red cells decomposes the hydrogen peroxide.

In the light of these studies it may be necessary to re-examine the reported deleterious effect of certain substances on PPLO. Unless the suspension media were up to the standards indicated by the work of Butler and Knight, the sensitivity of the PPLO may have been overrated. Without going into the details of the experimental methods, substances which according to the literature are noxious to PPLO will now be mentioned.

Keller et al. (1952) have shown that PPLO are very susceptible to the action of ordinary hand soap.

In my laboratory it has been found that the washing of glassware with some detergents, even though followed by thorough rinsing, had a completely inhibitory effect on the growth of all our PPLO stock cultures.

It is generally known that high concentrations of agar-agar (over 2%) are unfavourable for the growth of PPLO; therefore soft and even "sloppy" agar have been recommended for their cultivation. Butler and Knight (1960b) and Lynn and Morton (1956), have shown that certain brands or even batches of agar-agar are unfavourable for the growth of PPLO. It is therefore recommended that the different batches and brands be tested.

Smith and Morton (1953) describe the inhibitory effect of some mammalian sera on PPLO when used in concentrations higher than 40%. They found rabbit, sheep and horse serum suitable for the enrichment of PPLO media, whereas guinea pig, steer and cow serum were inferior. We found human serum excellent for the cultivation of human strains. According to Smith and Morton, the inhibitory action of bovine serum seems to be associated with its alpha-globulin; this action is enhanced by the presence of complement. However, it has to be realized that the various PPLO species differ in their preference for a particular serum and that they can become so adapted to growing on one mammalian serum that they do not tolerate a sudden change.

## C.   Therapeutic Substances

A considerable amount of work has been done on the action of therapeutics in PPLO diseases. Witt (1925) was the first to report the value of organic arsenical compounds in treating bovine pleuropneumonia. Bridré *et al.* (1928) described the specific action of stovarsol, an organic arsenical compound, on agalactia of sheep. However, the dose and the number of subcutaneous injections had to be restricted to avoid toxic effects on the animals. Pigoury (1938) reported that stovarsol cured mastitis and arthritis caused by the organism of agalactia. A number of authors studied the therapeutic effect of various compounds on the so-called polyarthritis of the rat and the chronic arthritis of mice. In these small rodents these joint conditions are caused by specific PPLO (Findlay *et al.* 1939; Klieneberger, 1939). It should be noted here that cures effected in these animals, although of interest, have no bearing on the treatment of the various human joint diseases which seem to have different causes. Findlay *et al.* (1939, 1940) studied organometallic compounds in rat polyarthritis and found that arsenical compounds and, to an even greater extent, gold compounds—in particular aurothioglucose, sodium auromaleate and sodium aurothiomaleate—had a curative effect. Sabin and Warren (1940) reported that inorganic and organic gold compounds of both the aliphatic and aromatic series influenced favourably the course of chronic PPLO arthritis in mice.

The sensitivity of PPLO to antibiotics *in vitro* and *in vivo* has been studied by many workers. The discovery that PPLO occur on human genitals and may be responsible for infectious conditions has stimulated interest in the effect of these substances on the organisms. A methodical study has recently been carried out in this field on a broad basis by Blyth (1958). We follow his report in the first instance. He tested the activity of 11 antibiotics as well as a mixture of three sulpha drugs against 47 human genital strains (Table V). He used solid medium for the test, because he found that tests in liquid media are unreliable owing to the faint turbidity of the broth culture and the necessity of making transfers on to solid media in order to measure the amount of growth. A colony count by the Miles and Misra method (1938), allows the direct reading of the result on the solid test plate. Each antibiotic was incorporated into solid medium in four different dilutions. The lowest concentration inhibiting growth completely was taken as the end point and called "minimal inhibitory concentration". An amount of $1 \cdot 0 \times 10^4$ to $4 \cdot 0 \times 10^4$ viable particles, suspended in phosphate buffered saline, made with high quality deionized water, was used as inoculum for each plate.

The rate of decay of each antibiotic during the experiments was determined by means of a sensitive bacterium. Results are not reliable unless this precaution is taken. It was thus shown that erythromycin and neomycin are remarkably stable substances, whereas chlortetracycline is very unstable. The degree of decay of the other tested substances was not so great as to interfere with the experiments.

All the human genital PPLO tested were insensitive to sulphonamides, penicillin, erythromycin and oleandomycin, whereas the other antibiotics inhibited their growth, and the tetracycline group was most effective. The high efficacy of oxytetracycline shown by Blyth had been reported previously in the literature by various workers, such as Leberman *et al.* (1950, 1952), Melén (1952), Robinson *et al.* (1952), Harkness and Bushby (1954) (see Table VI). However, the results of

TABLE V*

Sensitivity of PPLO to Antibiotics

| Antibiotic | Total strains tested | Number of strains sensitive to concentration of antibiotic shown | | | | | | | | | | | |
|---|---|---|---|---|---|---|---|---|---|---|---|---|---|
| | | 0.125 | 0.25 | 0.5 | 1.0 | 2 | 4 | 8 | 16 | 32 | 64 | 1000 | 4000[1] |
| Tetracycline | 44 | 0 | 15 | 44 | | | | | | | | | |
| Oxytetracycline | 45 | | 0 | 9 | 45 | | | | | | | | |
| Chlortetracycline | 47 | | | | 1 | 21 | 42 | 47 | | | | | |
| Chloramphenicol | 47 | | | | | | 0 | 6 | 47 | | | | |
| Streptomycin[2] | 47 | | | | | | 0 | 2 | 12 | 46 | 47 | | |
| Spiromycin | 47 | | | | | | | 1 | 14 | 38 | 47 | | |
| Neomycin | 47 | | | | | | | 0 | 6 | 47 | | | |
| Erythromycin | 47 | | | | | | | | | | | 0 | 1 |
| Oleandomycin | 46 | | | | | | | | | | | 0 | |
| Penicillin | 47 | | | | | | | | | | | | 0 |
| "Sulphatriad" | 46 | | | | | | | | | | | | 0 |
| Sigmamycin[3] | 24 | 0 | 2 | 22 | | | | | | | | | |

[1] Concentrations of antibiotics given in µg./ml. except penicillin which is in units/ml.
[2] Strains recorded as "sensitive" to streptomycin all showed resistant colonies
[3] Concentration of tetracycline only.
*    Table 20 in Blyth's thesis (1958)

some workers (Leberman *et al.*, Harkness and Bushby) with chlortetracycline differ widely from those of Melén and Blyth, because these two authors have taken its instability into account (Table VI). As a matter of fact it can be shown that chlortetracycline is as efficient as the other tetracyclines when the time of the tests is shortened.

All the strains tested contained streptomycin-resistant individuals and the resistance increased when cultivation took place in the presence of this antibiotic. Under similar conditions, resistance to tetra-

### TABLE VI*

Inhibition of PPLO by Antibiotics *in Vitro*

Summary of reports

Minimal Inhibitory Concentrations of Antibiotics†

| Author and date | Type of medium used | Number of strains | Tetra-cycline | Oxytetra-cycline | Chlortetra-cycline | Chlor-amphe-nicol | Strepto-mycin | Spiro-mycin | Neomycin | Erythro-mycin | Penicillin |
|---|---|---|---|---|---|---|---|---|---|---|---|
| Leberman *et al.* | | | | | | | | | | | |
| 1950 | liquid | 15 | | | | 15-100 | 0.1-15 | | | | >1000 |
| 1952 | liquid | 8 | | 0.1-0.5 | 25-200 | | | | | | |
| Melén 1952 | liquid | 20 | | 0.16-0.63 | 0.3-1.25 | 2.5-10 | 5-10 2-128 most strains | | | | >800 |
| Robinson *et al.* 1952 | solid | 28 | | 0.5-2.0 | 2-16 | 4-16 | 8-16 | | | | ≥51200 |
| Keller and Morton 1953 | liquid | 3 | | | | | | | | >200 | |
| Harkness and Bushby 1954 | solid | 6 | 1.5-3.0 | 0.4-1.5 | 25-50 | 12-25 | 10-40 | | | 100-150 | >1000 |
| Blyth 1958 | solid | 47 | 0.25-0.5 | 0.5-1.0 | 1-4 | 4-8 | 8-16 | 4-16 | 8-16 | >64 | >1000 |

*Table 23 in Blyth's thesis (1958).
†Concentrations of antibiotics are given in µg./ml. except penicillin which is given in units/ml.

cycline could also be slightly increased. Table V (Blyth, 1958) shows very clearly the sensitivity of 47 human genital PPLO to the antibiotics tested and the slight variations occurring in different strains.

It is of great interest to compare the efficacy of the antibiotics *in vitro* with their therapeutic effect *in vivo*.

It is well known that when bacteria occur in conjunction with PPLO, antibiotics such as penicillin or erythromycin may cure the bacterial infection but the PPLO remain. Thus Rubin *et al.* (1954) showed that gonorrhoea was cured with erythromycin, but all the patients from whom PPLO were cultivated before treatment, still harboured them after treatment. The residual PPLO may account for the fact that patients cured of gonorrhoea often develop non-gonococcal urethritis after the cure has been effected. Carlson *et al.* (1951) reported that penicillin did not cure a patient with meningitis whose cerebro-spinal fluid yielded not only meningococci, but also PPLO. Stokes' three cases of PPLO infection in which penicillin was ineffective but chlortetracycline curative, will be referred to again in Chapter X. Ovarian abscesses caused by PPLO have been cleared successfully by chlortetracycline (Gotthardson and Melén, 1953). Krücken (1959) published an interesting case of a paraurethritis caused by PPLO which was cured within a week with oxytetracycline.

Treatment with antibiotics to which PPLO are sensitive is very often given to patients with non-gonococcal urethritis. As shown by Harkness (1950) this condition may have many different causes, some infective and some non-infective. Because a differential diagnosis is very difficult and in fact is usually not attempted, and because a number of cases clear up spontaneously, the effect of the treatment can hardly be assessed and consequently the reports on the treatment of this condition are controversial. However, I believe that if acute cases, positive for PPLO, were selected, it could be shown that a high percentage of them would be cured by tetracycline treatment.

# CHAPTER X

# Serology, Immunology and Pathogenicity of Pleuropneumonia-like Organisms

It is proposed to discuss in this chapter different aspects of the host parasite relationship: A. The practical outcome of typing the various species of PPLO by means of hyperimmune rabbit sera; B. Immune reactions of the host infected with PPLO; C. The apparent picture of PPLO pathogenicity; and D. PPLO occurring in man and their possible significance.

## A. TYPING OF STRAINS BY SEROLOGICAL METHODS

It is very difficult to distinguish the various species of PPLO. Although certain differences exist in their type of growth, colony appearance, morphology, nutritional requirements, etc., these properties are neither outstanding enough nor sufficiently constant to be used for purposes of differentiation. It is, for example, a fact that the organism of pleuropneumonia of goats grows more quickly and in larger colonies than any other organism of the PPLO group. It is further known that the organism from the lung of the rat usually produces a rough colony without a marked centre, whereas the rat arthritis organism as a rule forms a granular colony with a markedly dense centre. It has further been observed that the organisms of pleuropneumonia of cattle and agalactia of sheep and goats, when grown in liquid, show at a certain stage of development, characteristic filamentous forms which are only rarely found in other species. All these properties are useful as guides but they are too dependent on the conditions of culture and on peculiarities of individual strains to be relied upon for purposes of identification.

It is a different proposition when we culture, for example, a PPLO from the lungs of bovidae suffering from pleuropneumonia and are able to produce characteristic lesions in cattle with the isolates. Under these circumstances it is justifiable to conclude that the organism of pleuropneumonia of cattle has been isolated. Diagnosis is not always so easy; it is often not possible to produce the disease with the isolated culture, either because we do not know the conditions under which infection might take place, or because we cannot experiment on human beings. On the other hand, the source of our culture may not be a lesion or we may be dealing with a saprophyte. PPLO have been cultured as contaminants from various bacterial cultures, from *Trichomonas vaginalis* and from all kinds of tissue cultures. Some workers have suggested that biochemical methods such as the fermentation of carbohydrates and

113

haemolysis, could be employed. However, according to my experience, reliable results cannot yet be obtained by these methods because the reactions are weak and take a long time to develop; above all, the results with various strains of the same species are not uniform.

Nutritional pathways may eventually provide useful methods for the classification of PPLO species (Knight, 1955). We know, for example, that the saprophytic species from soil and sewage are much less exacting in their nutritional requirements than the parasitic ones. We know further that the human genital organism may be very exacting. However, a lot more biochemical work has to be done before nutritonal and metabolic differences can be used for diagnostic purposes.

At the moment, it seems that the only reliable methods for the diagnosis of the various species of PPLO are serological ones. Three techniques have been mainly used for the purpose. Edward and Fitzgerald (1954) recommended a very simple method, viz. "the inhibition of growth test"; they incorporated "sufficient" inactivated rabbit antiserum (concentration between 1 : 25 and 1 : 1000) into a horse serum agar medium before pouring a plate and inoculated the organism to be tested on to the surface; they compared the growth obtained with a similar plate not containing antiserum; too large an inoculum has to be avoided. This method did not work consistently in my laboratory; some antisera which gave high titres in other tests did not show the inhibition at all, whilst others which produced the inhibition lost this property on storage. Therefore this method, though theoretically interesting, is not reliable enough for routine serological tests with strains of unknown origin. It has the additional drawback of requiring a considerable amount of antiserum, particularly if concentrations of, for example, 1 : 25 have to be used in the plates.

An agglutination test was first devised by Klieneberger (1938, 1940) for the differentiation of species. Cultures grown in liquid medium were spun down, washed and injected intravenously into rabbits. Fairly thick suspensions had to be used and many injections given in order to prepare a suitable antiserum.

Preparation of the antigen for the test met with great difficulties. After thorough trituration the final washed sediment was resuspended in a formalized buffer solution. The result was not always satisfactory because, although many suspensions were stable, some showed flocculation in the controls and had to be discarded. It was, however, possible to demonstrate that the sixteen strains examined belonged to seven different serological types, though the end-titres determined by the agglutination tests were on the low side compared with those of the complement fixation test described below.

This test has recently been adopted in my laboratory for the typing of PPLO from various sources. The preparation of the antigen will be described in detail as it is of general interest, but the test itself will be only briefly set out as it has been recorded in full detail by Card (1959).

## 1. *Preparation of Antigens*

A liquid medium is greatly improved by the presence of solid agar medium either floating about in it or attached to one of the glass surfaces (see also Edward, 1954). Therefore, an agar surface is produced at the bottom of a 1000 ml. conical flask from 15 ml. ox heart infusion agar enriched with 5 ml. of serum. Then 500 ml. of liquid medium (trypsin-digest-broth plus 20% serum, yeast and DNA as described in Chapter IV) are poured into this flask. The serum chosen depends on the species of PPLO used for the preparation of the antigen. Rabbit serum should be used for the growth of antigen injected into rabbits, and it is advisable to pass the strain several times in rabbit serum broth if it has been previously maintained on media containing serum from a different species; the inoculum used is one ml. of an overnight broth culture. Many strains, such as those from the lungs of rats and mice, all the human genital strains, the organisms of pleuropneumonia bovis and of agalactia of sheep and goats, grow better when aerated by shaking while under incubation. Others, such as the buccal strains, grow better under anaerobic conditions. An incubation time of 5 to 6 days produces a suitable antigen; the addition of penicillin is advisable to inhibit growth of contaminants. In spite of this a careful examination for purity should be carried out at the end of the incubation period. The culture is filtered through gauze, centrifuged at 8500 **g.** for 30 minutes and the deposit resuspended in 80 ml. of normal saline and spun again in two equal portions. The deposit from one portion is resuspended, by means of grinding in a Griffith tube, in 10 to 12 ml. of normal saline. Merthiolate to a concentration of 1 : 10,000 is added; this "fresh" suspension is called the F antigen. The second deposit is resuspended in 10 to 12 ml. of distilled water and boiled in a brine bath at 108°C for 10 minutes; sodium chloride to a concentration of 0·85% and merthiolate to 1 : 10,000 are added; this boiled preparation is called the B antigen. It seems probable that a heat-labile and a heat-stable antigen are present in PPLO; but antigen analysis has so far not been carried out. Finally, the antigens are standardized in the Hilger Biochemical Absorptiometer (see Card, 1959).

## 2. *Preparation of Antisera*

The organisms are grown in 500 ml. of liquid medium as described above. They are washed and resuspended in 18 ml. of saline, and the following portions are injected at intervals of 48 hours : 1 ml., 1 ml.,

2 ml., 2 ml., 4 ml., 5–6 ml. The rabbits are bled eight days after the last injection and if the titre of the antiserum is not as high as desired, a second course of injections is given after a fortnight's rest. The rabbits remain healthy during the courses of injections and do not lose weight.

## 3. *The Tests*

These are carried out in 3 × 3/8" tubes using 0·2 ml. as the unit volume. The five unit volumes, namely serum dilution, complement, antigen, lysin and blood corpuscles, bring the entire volume of each tube to one ml. A calcium–magnesium saline* is used for the dilutions. The tubes containing saline, complement and antigen (for the complement titration) and the tubes containing serum dilutions, complement and antigen (for the actual test) are kept at 4°C for 18 hours and then at room temperature for one hour; finally the haemolytic system is added. After a further incubation at 37°C for 30 minutes the tubes are centrifuged and read. Twice the amount of complement which allows lysis of 50% of the red cells in the complement titration test is used in the main complement fixation test. All sera are tested in doubling dilutions; the dilution giving 50% fixation is taken as the end titre of the serum.

It is of interest and importance to note that most of the normal rabbit (and also guinea-pig) sera gave an unspecific reaction in our tests in serum dilutions of 1 : 40 to 1 : 160. Rat and human sera do not give such reactions in the most concentrated dilution (1 : 10) used by us. These differences have to be taken into consideration when results are read.

## 4. *Results of Typing by Complement Fixation Tests*

It has been shown by Card (1959) and Lemcke (unpublished), that strains from different animals and also strains from different locations were distinct, and strains of common origin were frequently identical serologically. Thus antigens from 68 human genital strains gave high positive titres with sera prepared from human genital strains. Human mouth strains on the other hand, have an antigen in common with human genital strains, but both have also a specific antigen which gives rise to a high titre reaction with a homologous serum. Therefore, human genital and human buccal strains can be well distinguished from each other by cross complement fixation tests (see Table 2 of Card's paper). The following example shows how an unknown strain was typed; it was obtained from Dr. Shepard under the name of "T"

* Normal saline augmented with 1.8 × 10⁻⁴ M CaCl₂, 0.9 × 10⁻⁴ M MgCl₂, 1.95 × 10⁻³ M boric acid, and 1.36 × 10⁻⁴ M sodium borate.

strain: A serum prepared in the rabbit with this strain was tested to-gether with a serum prepared from a human genital strain designated "56", against the following 6 antigens: "T" strain, "56", mouse lung strain, rat lung strain, rat joint strain, chicken strain "X 95".

TABLE VII

| Antisera | Antigens | | | | | |
|----------|-----------|-----------|-----------|-----------|-----------|-----------|
| | "T" strain | "56" human genital strain | mouse lung strain | rat lung strain | rat joint strain | X 95 from chicken coryza |
| "T" | **10240** | 320 | 320 | 320 | 320 | 10240 |
| "56" | 320 | **5120** | 160 | 320 | 160 | 320 |

Bold figures = titres with homologous serum

This table shows that the "T" strain antigen and the "X 95" strain antigen reacted in an identical way with the two antisera used in the test. To confirm this further, a serum was prepared with the "X 95" strain and it was found that it reacted with the six antigens in the same way as the "T" serum. "X 95" is a chicken coccobacilliform body strain and therefore the conclusion was justified that the "T" strain belonged to the species of chicken coccobacilliform bodies, which some workers classify with the PPLO, although the author is of the opinion that it should be excluded from this group and regarded as a different type of organism (see Chapter VI). The serological typing of the "T" strain as a coccobacilliform body strain was further supported by morphological, tinctorial and cultural features characteristic of this species.

## B.  IMMUNE REACTIONS OF THE HOST INFECTED WITH PPLO

It has been known for a long time that in pleuropneumonia of cattle and agalactia of sheep and goats, specific antibodies against the infective organism are found in the blood serum of the host. Agglutination and complement fixation tests have been used with success for the field testing of animals (Campbell and Turner, 1936). The developing immunity of the vaccinated animals has likewise been followed up by serological methods among which C.F.T. seems to be the method of choice. In recent years this method has been introduced for the detection of antibodies against PPLO in human sera. Such antibodies have been found in patients suffering from infections of the genito-urinary system and PPLO were grown simultaneously from the lesions. However, PPLO were also grown where antibodies could not be found. Therefore, the question must be raised whether or not the appearance of antibodies in the blood of man or animals is a specific response to a special PPLO infection. In order to solve this problem, we have carried out a great number of cultural and serological investigations in small laboratory animals and investigations have also been carried out in healthy and diseased human beings.

## 1. *Infections Attributed to PPLO in Chickens*

Some workers have thought that the PPLO isolated from chickens were the culprits causing chronic respiratory disease (C.R.D.). However, in order to prove that an isolate is pathogenic for chickens, it must be studied in animal experiments, in serological reactions as well as culturally and tinctorially. As C.R.D. starts with rhinitis and may later affect the air sac, attempts were made to produce the disease in healthy birds by introducing the isolated PPLO into the nasal passages. It was not possible to infect healthy chickens with any of the various PPLO strains isolated from these birds. In contrast to this, coccobacilliform bodies isolated from cases of C.R.D. (Nelson, 1936 a, b, c) caused inflammation of the nasal passages and rhinitis or coryza. The serological tests are in accordance with these findings.

## 2. *Infections Attributed to PPLO in Rats*

It has been known for a long time that laboratory rats are prone to bronchiectasis which, as already described, may be acute, although more often chronic and frequently only fully established in old rats. As mentioned before it was shown by Klieneberger-Nobel and Cheng (1955) that any young rat with apparently healthy lungs will develop an acute and quickly progressive bronchiectasis when a bronchus is ligated and a large number of PPLO colonies of the rat lung strain can be grown from the lesions.

As mentioned in Chapter II Section C, the serological tests provided further interesting information about rat bronchiectasis. Very few young rats showed a low antibody titre in their serum. Young adult rats showed a titre which increased with age. The titres were quite specific, for the sera did not react with the antigen from a rat polyarthritis strain nor with PPLO antigens from other sources. However, the titres of sera from bronchiectatic rats, although specific, are never very high; this is probably due to the localization of the disease. Infections with the polyarthritis strain take quite a different course. About the spontaneous naturally-occurring polyarthritis caused by this strain, Findlay *et al.* (1939) write as follows: "The joints most commonly affected are the tibiotarsal and the radiocarpal; less frequently the intertarsal or phalangeal joints are swollen. In the spontaneous disease, it is not uncommon to see three or all four of the limbs involved. The first signs of swelling of an affected joint are accompanied by a glistening appearance of the skin, which is smooth and pearl-coloured. Often these appearances are localized to one small nodule. Later the whole region of the joint takes on a pink and even purplish tint and is slightly oedematous. This condition may eventually subside, leaving some thickening round the joint; or, while the joint is still swollen, the skin may ulcerate and the limb below the joint may be

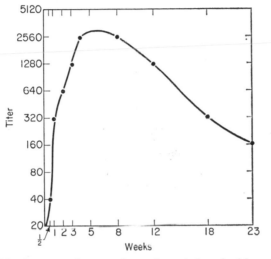

FIG. 40. Logarithmic curve of serum titres of rats infected with a rat polyarthritis strain. (First published by Klieneberger-Nobel, 1960).

gnawed off by the rat. The skin can be easily stripped off affected joints in the early stages, showing in the case of the tibiotarsal joint a fusi-form swelling, of a pearly colour. On cutting the swollen tissues straw-coloured fluid may be liberated". From the diseased joints a pleuro-pneumonia-like organism was cultured which was characterized by a finely–granular colony with a pronounced centre. When a suspension of the culture was injected into the foot-pad, polyarthritis started to develop 4 to 6 days after the injection; the disease may take a severe course with fatal outcome (Klieneberger, 1939). On the other hand, when the organism, together with agar as an adjuvant, is injected sub-cutaneously, a lump can be felt at the place of injection after some days; this soon develops into a capsulated abscess containing a considerable amount of pus. The rats become very sluggish and seem ill but cure themselves within 3 to 6 weeks when the abscess breaks through the skin and clears. During the first fortnight the spleen is invariably grossly enlarged and the organism can be cultured from the blood, the spleen, some glands and often from the kidneys. This all goes to show that the rat polyarthritis PPLO produces a systemic disease. It is therefore not surprising that during the disease the antibody titre against the specific organism rises steeply and end titres of 1 : 2000 to 1 : 5000 are commonly reached during the first weeks of the infection. Even when the abscess has cleared and organisms are no longer found, the serum titre remains high for some time and decreases only gradually. In Fig. 40 a logarithmic curve showing the rise and fall of the titre in a typical infection experiment can be seen.

If older rats are chosen for an infection experiment with a rat polyarthritis strain in the way described, the development of the abscess and the rise of the serum titre takes a similar course to that in young animals (lesst han 2–3 months old) but because the older rats are likewise suffering from pulmonary disease, the serum will react to a high titre with the polyarthritis strain and to a low titre with the rat lung strain.

## 3. *Infections Attributed to PPLO in Mice*

A number of authors have isolated PPLO cultures from mice, for example Findlay *et al.* (1938, 1939), Sabin and Johnson (1940), Sabin (1941), Edward (1940), Mooser (1949, 1951); see also Edward's and Klieneberger-Nobel's reviews of 1954. In spite of all this work the significance of these organisms and the number of different species isolated is not fully known. The following naturally developing conditions, supposed to be caused by PPLO in these rodents, have been described: conjunctivitis, rhinitis, pneumonia or bronchopneumonia, joint disease and a nervous condition with its seat in the brain called "rolling disease". The various strains isolated in the first place are no longer available and can therefore not be typed serologically.

However, as described in Chapter II it has been found that a pneumonia can be established in mice within 10 to 14 days by intranasal insufflation of unspecific material. From the resulting lesions which usually present themselves as consolidations, a PPLO, "the mouse lung strain" has been repeatedly isolated (Edward, 1940, 1947a). This resembles the rat lung strain in its colony appearance and is serologically related, but perhaps not identical to it. Pneumonic conditions caused by the mouse lung strain also occur spontaneously in stock mice. Specific antibodies can be demonstrated in the blood of the infected mice and the amount seems to be related to the extent of the infection (Lemcke, in the press) which may be confined to the nasopharynx or producing lesions in the lungs.

By passaging various infective agents such as the virus of yellow fever, the virus of choriomeningitis and the protozoon Toxoplasma intracerebrally from mouse to mouse, another species of PPLO has been "lighted up" in different laboratories as reported in Chapter II. This organism, "the mouse brain strain" (formerly designated "L5" by Klieneberger) seems to be serologically distinct from the mouse lung strain. These two organisms are also different in their pathogenicity, the one causing rolling disease, the other pneumonia.

## 4. Infections Possibly due to PPLO in other Animals

PPLO have been suspected of causing a number of disease conditions in domestic animals such as cows, dogs, pigs, sheep and goats (Edward, 1950; Chu and Beveridge, 1954; Switzer, 1953, 1955; Carter and McKay, 1953; Whittlestone, 1957; and Chu, 1960). There is even a report on a PPLO isolated from a chameleon (Klinge, 1954). The animals concerned have so far not been examined for specific antibodies, nor have the strains been typed serologically. Therefore the significance of these strains can so far not be appraised.

## 5. Infections Attributed to PPLO in Humans

As reported in Chapter II mainly three specific types of PPLO occur in man, namely the buccal, the "G" which Ruiter and Wentholt (1955) cultured from gangrenous lesions and the human genital. From reports such as those of Huijsmans-Evers and Ruys (1956a), it seems probable that saprophytic strains may occasionally be found on human genitals. However, among a large number of strains isolated by us not a single one was of this type and only one was found that differed at all in serological structure from the human genital type. Nicol and Edward (1953) found that all except one of their strains belonged to the same human genital type as our strains. A second human type may sometimes occur in America represented by the "Campo strain". It can therefore be concluded that the PPLO by far the most frequently found on human genitalia belong to one type and are serologically uniform.

Cultural and serological tests were carried out in my laboratory (Card 1959, Klieneberger-Nobel, 1959a, b, 1960b) in order to study the significance of the commonest human genital type. As controls for the cultural tests we examined two male groups of persons: (a) Adults of a high hygienic standard; and (b) boys under the age of 13 years of age. In one hundred men of group (a) PPLO were found three times; in 47 boys of group (b) PPLO were not demonstrated. In contrast to this were the results in male venereal patients. PPLO were isolated in 31 out of 65 cases (48%) of acute and sub-acute non-gonococcal urethritis (N.G.U.). From 49 cases of untreated gonorrhoea 15 (30%) were PPLO positive. In chronic and cured N.G.U., PPLO were not found. Female venereal cases yielded even more PPLO positive results. In untreated and treated gonorrhoea the percentage was very high (87–90%). Similarly high positive results were obtained from cases of cervicitis and/or vaginitis and/or urethritis. However, symptomless cases were negative.

A search, by complement fixation test (C.F.T.) for antibodies against human genital PPLO in the blood of a large number of men and women, resulted in even more interesting findings. As controls, 297 men and women blood donors from the N.W. London Transfusion centre were examined. 1·1% of the males and 3·7% of the females were positive. As a second control group, children under 13 years of age were tested; 2 out of 104 sera from children were positive (approximately 2%). In contrast to this was the result obtained from 700 sera of V.D. clinic patients. Of these 34·2% were positive, viz. 18·7% of the males and 44·5% of the females. In contrast to this, only 6·1% of 198 medical out-patients had PPLO positive sera and 6·3% of 96 antenatal patients in a country district. The serological findings show that a high percentage of positive PPLO titres are found in groups which often suffer from venereal disease and from which also PPLO have been cultured most frequently. These results are supported by observations on a number of infections in human patients; PPLO were demonstrated by culture from the lesions and rising antibody titres were observed during the period of disease (Stokes, 1955; Lemcke, unpublished studies). From the animal experiments and the results in human beings, it is justifiable to conclude that a causal relationship exists between the occurrence in the blood of antibodies directed against a specific PPLO and its significance as an agent of disease. Several other authors such as Harkness (1950), Stokes (1955), Berg et al. (1957, 1960) also regard the human genital PPLO type as a potential pathogen. Other workers believe that its significance is questionable.

## C. The Apparent Picture of PPLO Pathogenicity

The problem of the establishment of an infection is extremely complex and has not yet been solved to any appreciable degree for any one of the known infectious diseases. Factors which depend on the infective agent and others which depend on the host, together with environmental ones, are certainly involved. However, it is known that some organisms, such as the plague bacillus or *Salmonella typhi*—when virulent—are far more agressive than some other organisms such as the pneumococcus. The incubation periods of the naturally acquired PPLO infections vary a great deal and there is little information about the modes of transfer and the reasons for the outbreak of epidemics. However, all the diseases caused by PPLO are difficult to establish when cultures of the agent are used. Even though pleuropneumonia of cattle is such a devastating disease, we do not really know how it spreads because, if diseased and healthy animals are experimentally brought into contact with each other, the results are quite erratic and in order to produce pleuropneumonia by means of a spray of a virulent culture, very massive doses have to be used. By subcutaneous or intra-muscular injections of organisms, extensive oedemas can be produced, but the disease proper does not develop.

In agalactia of sheep and goats the organism may remain latent for many months in the ewes, but the disease breaks out when the animals are weakened by parturition and lactation.

Bronchiectasis in rats is caused by a PPLO that, as an inhabitant of the nasopharynx, causes little harm in very young rats. When the rats are weakened by an operation or after the ligation of a bronchus, the organisms appear in the lungs and cause a condition that progresses rapidly and leads to the death of the animals. Otherwise, a chronic lung disease develops when the rats are ageing.

It can be difficult to infect rats experimentally by means of a suspension of the specific organism of rat polyarthritis. However, when an adjuvant such as agar is added, an intravenous injection may cause a severe polyarthritis, or if injected with agar subcutaneously an abscess arises.

As already seen the neurotropic agent in mice can be "lighted up" by passage of unspecific material intracerebrally, and can then cause the serious condition, rolling disease; and the pneumotropic agent can be activated by nasal insufflation of irritant materials. These PPLO are probably not present in every mouse, but if sufficient animals are used, the conditions rolling disease and pneumonia respectively can be established in a few by applying such stimuli. Once established these infections can be transferred from mouse to mouse, the rolling disease by intracerebral passages, the pneumonia by nasal insufflation of a suspension of diseased tissue.

As has been pointed out a number of workers are of the opinion that some genital infections and in particular N.G.U. in the male are caused by the common human genital type of PPLO. Here again mere presence of the organism may not suffice to establish the disease. Recently the history of a case of paraurethritis in a male was published by Krücken (1959). A student had intercourse with a promiscuous female without ill effect. About three months later he had a forced coitus with a virgin, causing considerable irritation. Eight days later he attended the clinic with an inflamed paraurethral canal ending in an abscess on the lower side of the penis. PPLO were obtained in pure culture from the lesions and after one week's oxytetracycline medication, cure was effected. This case-history suggests that mechanical irritation had triggered off a previously latent PPLO infection.

The opinion that a second factor or factors are instrumental in establishing PPLO infections is further supported by work initiated by Mooser (1945, 1949, 1951). He found that mouse PPLO which did not grow by themselves in the peritoneal cavity of these rodents, grew abundantly in the exudate when they had been injected together with ectromelia virus. The PPLO also appeared in the spleen and liver of these mice. Schauwecker (1947), in Mooser's laboratory, activated both the neurotropic and the pneumotropic variety of PPLO in mice by injection of ectromelia. It was even possible to establish a human PPLO strain in the mouse peritoneum in conjunction with ectromelia (Mooser and Joos, 1952). Klieneberger-Nobel (1954) was able to establish a strain of the organism of agalactia and a virulent strain of pleuropneumonia of cattle in the mouse peritoneum together with ectromelia. However, similar attempts failed completely with saprophytic PPLO and with a non-virulent old laboratory strain of pleuropneumonia of cattle. This shows that pathogenicity comes into the picture. Nasemann et al. (1954) and Nasemann and Röckl (1960) showed that the growth of a human genital PPLO in embryonated eggs was stimulated not only by ectromelia but also by vaccinia, neurolapine and myxomatosis viruses.

All these records go to show that secondary factors play an important part in transforming a seemingly harmless, or a latent PPLO, into a pathogen.

## D.   PPLO Occurring in Man and their Possible Significance

The role that PPLO play in human disease has not yet been settled. It is a difficult but also a most interesting question. Because the problem of the pathogenicity of PPLO for human beings is such a very controversial subject and may interest the bacteriologist as well as the venereologist, it is perhaps permissible here to go into greater detail than in the previous chapters. I shall try to construct a picture of the position from the literature and from my own experience. In the first place I shall examine the possible significance of PPLO in non-gonococcal urethritis (N.G.U.) in men, and then in genital infection in a wider sense.

### 1.  *Non-gonococcal Urethritis*

If a person not familiar with the subject were to read all the papers concerned, his state of mind would become one of utter confusion. The reasons for this will be evident if only the most important papers on the subject are read. The authors concerned have put a great deal of effort and thought into their work. However, no two of them have had similar results, because no two of them used the same media for the isolation of the PPLO, the same methods for the identification of the colonies, and for the collection of the samples and transfer to the culture media, nor has the selection of patients and controls been carried out from a similar viewpoint. To make things worse, some figures are quoted out of their context and may thus create a wrong impression. For example, Nicol and Edward (1953) quote correctly that Harkness and Henderson-Begg (1948) isolated PPLO from 14% of their cases of N.G.U. However, they do not point out that these figures represent a summary of 253 cases including N.G.U. in association with arthritis. The 253 cases were further subdivided by the authors into bacterial and abacterial urethritis and into venereal and non-venereal urethritis. Harkness and Henderson-Begg differentiated their cases very carefully on clinical and laboratory findings with the result that 5 out of 10 (50%) cases of acute abacterial urethritis and 21 out of 57 (38%) of subacute or Waelsch urethritis, gave positive cultures. Freundt, in 1958, quotes a figure of 17% for Harkness and Henderson-Begg's positives. However, these 7 positives were found among "41 cases of arthritis complicating abacterial urethritis (so-called Reiter's disease)". Here again a wrong impression is created by the figure referred to. It only goes to show that in the literature on N.G.U. almost nothing can be taken at its face value. However, when proper allowances are made for diversities of methods, a good deal of valuable information can be extracted from these papers. Therefore, we shall now analyse the methods and results more closely.

## (a) Media for Isolation

Dienes (1940) used "a boiled blood medium" enriched with 30% ascitic fluid. Beveridge, Campbell and Lind (1946) used a medium described by Beveridge (1943) as a meat liver medium (the "V.F." medium of Campbell and Turner (1936)) devised for the cultivation of the organism of pleuropneumonia bovis enriched with 30% horse serum with sulphanilamide added to some of it for the suppression of bacteria. Salaman (1946) used a 10% "chocolate agar"; "no adjustment of pH was found necessary". The medium of Harkness and Henderson-Begg was composed as follows: a papain digest of ox heart served as the base with the addition of 10% yeast extract and 20% horse serum. It was used in the form of a sloppy agar with penicillin and thallium acetate added in appropriate amounts. If growth occurred in the sloppy agar this was transferred to plates. Nicol and Edward (1953) used an ox heart infusion enriched with 1% peptone, 10% yeast extract, 20% horse serum as well as penicillin and thallium acetate. Melén and Odeblad (1951, 1952) used a meat infusion peptone agar with 30% horse serum and varying amounts of penicillin and "sulfa- metin" supplied by placing a drop of each solution near the edge of the plate. Klieneberger-Nobel (1959a, b) used a "boiled blood medium" made from an ox heart infusion peptone agar enriched with 20% pooled, inactivated human serum, 0·5% Oxoid yeast extract, 20 μgr/ ml. of deoxyribonucleic acid (D.N.A.), 5% filtrate of a staphylococcus broth culture, 100 units of penicillin per ml. and thallium acetate to a concentration of 1 : 4000.

Not all of these media are equally good, though some of the human strains will grow on all of them. We know that the various species of PPLO are different in their nutritional requirements. The sapro- phytic species (Laidlaw and Elford's strains) are much less exacting than any of the other types and they will develop on a fairly rich meat medium without serum. Among the pathogenic strains the organism of pleuropneumonia of goats is the easiest to grow, followed by the organ- ism of pleuropneumonia of cattle. They both develop satisfactorily on an ordinary meat infusion peptone agar with as little as 5% serum, whereas the organism of agalactia of sheep requires a higher percent- age of serum. The rat and mouse strains need, in addition, some vita- mins which are supplied in a "boiled blood medium". Edward (1950) found that his P strains from the genitals of cattle were more exacting than the other known animal strains. Yeast extract and D.N.A. sup- plied the additionally required growth factors. When I embarked on the study of N.G.U., I investigated the influence of various substances on the growth of a number of human strains and found that they be- haved individually. Some of them grew on a medium enriched with horse serum, but others would not grow unless horse serum was re- placed by human serum for which ascitic fluid can probably be sub- stituted, although it has to be kept in mind that ascitic fluids vary widely. I found further that yeast extract and D.N.A. as recommended by Edward, improved the media greatly. I used 0·5% yeast extract and found that much higher concentrations had an inhibitory effect. On a medium thus enriched, the strains of human origin could be cultivated well as a rule, but a few still refused to develop or grew as tiny colonies without peripheral zones. When a sterile filtrate of a staphylococcus culture was added, the growth of these few was much improved.

All PPLO require a more or less soft medium for growth and a small amount of agar enhances their growth in broth. Aeration speeds the growth of human genital strains in liquid media. However, when a human genital strain was cultured for several passages in tissue culture (amnion cells and HeLa cells) (Blyth, 1958), it grew on artificial media only under anaerobic conditions.

It will be seen from this digression that some workers who tried to isolate PPLO under unsuitable conditions could not obtain as high a number of positives from their cases as others who gave the organisms a better chance to develop. In spite of this, the number of positives obtained in one group of people may bear a correct relationship to the number of positives found in a different group.

## (b) *Identification of Organisms*

Some authors, such as Salaman (1946), Salaman and his collaborators (1946), have used an opaque medium ("chocolate agar") and stained their growth by the Bouin-Giemsa method devised by Klieneberger-Nobel (1950). This is not a reliable method when *mixed growth* of bacterial and PPLO colonies has developed. The bacteria are easily lifted from the underlying agar and may float over very small PPLO colonies and obscure them. The best method is to use a transparent medium and to inspect the growth with the low power of the microscope ( ×30–100) and to light up the field of vision evenly by using the substage condenser with the top lens unscrewed; even the smallest colonies are seen by this method. Confirmatory subculture of characteristic colonies on solid and into liquid media without bacteriostatic substances should be carried out. For further confirmation staining methods should then be applied to the pure culture and here the Bouin-Giemsa method is very suitable.

## (c) *Transport and Transfer of Specimens*

The transport of material from the clinic to the laboratory and then the transfer to the media is very important. Some authors have used cotton wool swabs which were inserted into "transport media" and after a delay of hours or more were used for the inoculation of the culture media. Obviously, this meant loss of viable organisms, particularly if the transport medium did not support the growth of the PPLO. The best method is the inoculation by means of a platinum loop directly from the patient on to the culture media. The media should be placed in the incubator as soon as possible, although a delay of a few hours will not reduce the number of organisms that will grow into colonies.

## (d) *The Taking of Specimens*

Some authors do not even describe their method of taking samples and this is one of the most important points to be considered. The urethra is, as Harkness (1950), points out, a sterile organ in the healthy male except for the orifice and its most anterior parts. These usually contain a very mixed saprophytic bacterial flora. There are, however, authors such as Freundt (1956) who report that they have taken their material with a cotton wool swab from the orifice and the prepuce. The results that Freundt obtained cannot be compared with those of authors who, after thorough cleansing of the orifice and the fossa navicularis with spirit, have inserted their "rigid" platinum loop two inches down the anterior urethra in order to take their specimen by scraping. Thorough cleansing of the exterior parts should certainly always precede the collecting of specimens from the male urethra, even if discharge or urine are used for the examination. No wonder that Freundt found in his specimens "a rich saprophytic bacterial flora", whereas Harkness and Henderson-Begg had such a large number of abacterial specimens.

## (e) *Selection of the Cases*

We now come to the most important point of all. There is such a diversity in the viewpoints which have led the various workers to select their cases, that for this reason alone it is not surprising the results of the examinations differ widely.

Non-gonococcal urethritis (N.G.U.) (often called non-specific urethritis) is not a defined disease. Under this name all inflammatory conditions of the urethra—with the exception of gonorrhoea—are grouped together artificially. From the venereologists we learn that this condition can have more than a dozen causes. Obviously, if PPLO are searched for without discrimination in all kinds of urethritis, some PPLO-positive cases will be found, but the information gained will be valueless. Very few authors have made a thorough clinical investigation of their cases in order to classify them as well as possible. As Harkness (1950) and Harkness and Henderson-Begg (1948) point out, such classification is not possible without urethroscopy. They distinguish between bacterial and abacterial urethritis and their cases of abacterial urethritis yield most of the PPLO cultures. However, these cases are subdivided again into 14 groups, of which only a few are quoted here, viz.: subacute urethritis of Waelsch type; acute urethritis simulating gonorrhoea; residual abacterial urethritis following successful penicillin therapy for gonorrhoea; traumatic (chemical) urethritis; urethrorrhoea (excess of mucus, epithelial cells, occasional leucocyte); spermatorrhoea; intrameatal condylomata accuminata, etc. Almost all their PPLO positive cases were in the first two groups, both comprising only primary attacks of urethritis. The patients with subacute urethritis of Waelsch type had a very mild form of urethritis with a longish incubation period; the urethroscopic picture showed many excrescences. The patients with acute urethritis had a copious discharge with a short incubation period; urethroscopy showed an inflamed and reddened mucosa. As most authors have not classified their cases properly, they have considerably lower numbers of positives in their urethritis cases than Harkness and Henderson-Begg. The discrepancy in the results is, however, even greater in the groups called "normal". Some workers used as controls volunteers from groups of young men (soldiers, police candidates . . . ) who were not clinically examined. To the results from these groups of men Harkness's criticism of Salaman and collaborators' results in "normal" men applies equally well: " . . . subacute urethritis, often symptomless, is easily overlooked and the evidence of this worker would have been more convincing if urethroscopy and smears after prostatovesicular massage had been carried out on all cases yielding positive cultures and any with evidence of urethritis eliminated from his control group". Harkness apparently selected his controls very carefully and it is therefore very significant that he had no positives among his 65 "normals" (50 men, 15 women).

Those workers who did not examine their controls clinically should at least have realized in dealing with a genital infection that exposure must play an important part, particularly as there are mild cases of urethritis which are difficult to recognize. They should have selected their normals from "a sexually circumspect" (see Berg, Weinberger and Dienes) rather than from a "sexually promiscuous" part of the population. The differences in the results from controls between Nicol and Edward (1953) on the one side and Klieneberger-Nobel (1959a, b) on the other side, are probably due to the fact that the first authors examined a group of young London police candidates, whereas the latter used boys under the age of 13 and adults with high hygienic standards.

The best descriptions of the kind of urethritis in which PPLO may play a significant role are given by Harkness and Henderson-Begg (1948): "Primary abacterial urethritis of venereal origin may be ushered in with signs and symptoms of either a subacute or an acute inflammation. Waelsch in 1901 was the first to describe the former, and in his original communication he stated that the disease was characterized by a long incubation period (in our experience from five to thirty days) mild subjective and objective symptoms, chronicity from the beginning and poor response to treatment. There is also a typical urethroscopic picture . . . which is characterized by . . . the presence of the small greyish-white semitransparent superficial and wedge-shaped excrescences . . . The acute type of abacterial urethritis of venereal origin may be indistinguishable clinically from acute gonorrhoea. The disease is characterized by a short incubation period (one to three days), an acute onset with profuse purulent or mucopurulent urethral discharge, and pain on micturition. Urethroscopy shows a red and inflamed mucous membrane with no infiltrations." This condition is rare. Harkness and Henderson-Begg collected 10 such cases of which 5 (50%) were positive whereas they collected 57 of the primary subacute type of which 21 (38%) were positive for PPLO. I am convinced that the number of positives would probably have been considerably higher if these two authors had used a more favourable medium for the isolation of the human genital PPLO, in particular if they had used human instead of horse serum. In spite of this, these results seem very significant when compared with the 65 carefully selected normal adults who were exclusively PPLO negative. In contrast to Harkness and Henderson-Begg, Klieneberger-Nobel used an excellent isolation medium, but the classification of her cases was not based on urethroscopy and thorough clinical examination. Nevertheless her acute and subacute cases (65—all primary) yielded (31) 48% PPLO positives. When compared with the number of her PPLO positives from normal males (47 boys under 13—no PPLO; 100 men of a high hygienic standard—3% positives), this seems a very significant result. The results of Nicol and Edward are not at all in disagreement with those of Harkness and Henderson-Begg and Klieneberger-Nobel. These authors have not divided up their patients according to Harkness' recommendation, yet they obtained 14 cultures of human genital PPLO in 52 (27%) of their abacterial urethritis cases. As they used horse serum media the percentage is probably too low. The number of their positives from 90 apparently healthy men, is 11%. As urethroscopy and smears after prostatovesicular massage was not carried out on the positive cases, it may be assumed that a number of these young police candidates were not "healthy" though they were found to have no "genital abnormality". Huijsmans-Evers and Ruys (1956b) who did not use an optimal medium (horse serum), isolated the human genital PPLO from 13 out of 26 cases of non-specific urethritis (50%). I do not discuss here the results of some of the earlier workers who used an inferior medium and did not classify their cases.

However, the results of two more recent workers are in complete disagreement with all the reports mentioned so far, and should be discussed. One of them is Freundt (1958) who obtained more PPLO cultures from his non-urethritis than from his urethritis cases. "The most conspicuous feature of this distribution is the lower frequency of *Mycoplasma* demonstrated in patients with manifest urethritis, whether gonococcal or not, than in men who either had no urethritis at all or at the most only showed microscopically recognizable signs of this." We have criticized already his method of taking specimens and of selecting cases. It should be added that he found his oral cultures were identical with his cultures from human genitals, whereas all other authors regard the mouth cultures, according to cultural and serological tests, as belonging to a different species designated *Mycoplasma salivarium* by Edward and Freundt (1956). Freundt (1958) also twice cultivated the organism of pleuropneumonia bovis from human beings.

The second author who has published results widely divergent from those generally reported, is Shepard (1956, 1957, 1958), who claimed that in a large proportion of his urethritis cases he found on his primary plates a PPLO organism appearing as very tiny colonies. In most cases he was not able to obtain subcultures from the colonies. When he passed these apparent colonies in embryonated eggs, he obtained after 15 passages a culture (T strain) that grew on PPLO media. As described earlier in this chapter I have found that this strain is identical with a strain of "chicken coccobacilliform bodies" discovered by Nelson and shown (see Chapter VI) to be the aetiological cause of C.R.D., which disease can be transferred through the egg. I believe it is a hazardous procedure to claim that appearances on primary plates are "cultures" when they cannot be established in subcultures.

## 2. *Other Conditions of the Urogenital Tract including Systemic Infections*

So far I have only reported on work undertaken to find out whether PPLO are likely to be the cause of N.G.U. and the results show that they play a role in some kinds of non-gonococcal urethritis. Yet PPLO have been found in many other conditions of men and women where their occurrence seems more definitely of pathological significance. Stokes (1955) isolated PPLO from the blood of a woman with an abacterial puerperal fever, from the wound and pleural fluid of a patient suffering from post-operative abacterial empyema, from high vaginal swabs in a second case of puerperal fever, and from a woman with hydrosalpinx and pyrexia. In three of these four patients specific antibody, demonstrated by complement fixation tests, appeared during the infection, reached a maximum titre at about three weeks during convalescence and thereafter fell. Strains from Stokes' patients were examined by Edward and diagnosed as type I human genital strains. This report of Stokes seems of great importance because it shows that in certain serious conditions PPLO were the only organisms found. In one woman who was running a high temperature they were found circulating in the blood.

Similarly interesting are the studies of Melén and his collaborators (Melén and Odeblad, 1950, 1952; Melén and Gotthardson, 1955). Using a C.F.T. they found fairly high serum titres in the blood of five women with salpingo-oophoritis against an antigen prepared from a human genital PPLO strain. The authors observed further that 76% of women with inflammatory pelvic disease harboured PPLO on their genitals, whereas only 19% of women free from such conditions were

PPLO positive. It is of particular interest that like Stokes, Melén and Gotthardson demonstrated a significant rise in titre during the salpingo-oophoritis and a decrease after recovery. Gotthardson and Melén (1953) reported further the isolation of pure cultures of PPLO from ovarian abscesses in two women. These findings confirm the earlier work carried out by Dienes *et al.* (1948) who cultured PPLO from Bartholin's abscesses in six cases, from a pelvic abscess associated with puerperal infection, and from an abscess associated with salpingitis.

Most workers have found that women harbour PPLO more frequently on their genitals than men (Dienes *et al.* 1948). This applies particularly to the women who attend venereal diseases clinics: I found that cultural examination for PPLO was positive in 33 (approx. 50%) of a total of 59 such women. In untreated and treated gonorrhoea and in cervicitis, vaginitis or urethritis the percentages of PPLO isolations were very high (87 to 90%). PPLO also occurred together with *Trichomonas vaginalis*. However, in 14 symptomless women and in others suffering from warts or genital ulcers only, PPLO were not found. Harkness and Henderson-Begg (1948) had similar results. Melén and Odeblad (1951) found 13 virgins free from PPLO. The cases reported with pyosalpinx, pelvic abscesses, puerperal sepsis in which PPLO were the only organisms found, show that they can be pathogenic.

In men also, very severe conditions can be associated with PPLO. In a very thorough paper Berg, Weinberger and Dienes (1957) describe an acute haemorrhagic cystitis (also called acute abacterial pyuria) with involvement of the upper and lower portions of the genitourinary tract and occasionally of eyes, joints and skin. They suggest that PPLO are the infective organisms. PPLO were present in the urine and disappeared during successful antibiotic therapy whereas bacteria were absent throughout. I quote the authors: "It seems probably that this type of infection of the bladder is a facet of a potentially generalized genito-urinary tract infection, but that it presents an especially dramatic clinical picture because of the intense inflammatory response ... The infection often originates in the urethra, spreads to the genital appendages and to the bladder, may obstruct the ureteral orifices by edema and ascend into the kidney, pelvis and parenchyma". Harkness and Henderson-Begg (1948) examined 8 cases of the same disease which Harkness calls "acute abacterial pyuria". They all presented the same cystoscopic picture and in 6 cases PPLO were found in the urines. He is convinced that the disease is venereal in origin. Of great interest is further the report on PPLO positive rectal cultures in males, also considered to be of venereal origin by Berg *et al.* (1960).

Though the aetiological cause of Reiter's disease is still unknown, it should be mentioned that PPLO have been isolated a few times from synovial fluids (see Warthin, 1948; Krücken and Fabry, 1955). It is possible that a patient suffering from Reiter's disease is also infected by PPLO. If so the PPLO may be carried from the local lesion by means of the blood stream into the diseased joints. That this can happen in animals has been demonstrated by Lemcke (in the press) who found a rat lung strain (usually causing localized infection of the lungs) in an abscess containing and caused by a serologically distinct rat strain. This may explain why PPLO of human genital type can sometimes be found in diseased joints in cases of Reiter's disease, although these organisms may not be the aetiological cause of Reiter's disease (see also Oates et al. 1959).

It has been seen that PPLO may be responsible for severe conditions in men and women. It is of particular interest that in those few cases where serological tests have been carried out, a rising and falling antibody titre has been demonstrated.

As we had no opportunity to examine the sera of hospitalized persons over longer periods of time, Card (1959) examined in my laboratory the occurrence of complement fixing antibodies to human genital PPLO in various classes of people, in the expectation that the incidence of antibodies would be related to the probability of infection.

Her results were as follows:

"Patients from venereal disease clinics had the highest incidence of antibodies (34 per cent.); blood donors and children had the lowest (2 per cent.); and medical, gynaecological, and antenatal out-patients, gave intermediate values. Among the V.D. clinic patients, antibodies were more frequent in women (45 per cent.). The distribution of antibodies was in accord with the frequency of venereal disease to be expected in the different groups of subjects investigated, and ran roughly parallel with the frequency with which PPLO could be isolated from the urogenital tract."

The pathogenicity of the G strain first isolated by Ruiter and Wentholt (1950, 1952, 1953) must also be considered. This was first isolated from a phagedaenic ulcer on the glans penis. Preparations from the pus showed fusiform bacilli and spirochaetes in addition to cocci. Innumerable PPLO colonies were grown from the pus. This same organism was found on three other occasions and each time in large numbers in men with fuso-spirillary gangrenous lesions of the genitals. The PPLO cultured in these four cases differs from the usual human genital type and the type frequently found in the mouth, in the following respects; it grows better anaerobically and is pathogenic for young mice. The same authors (1955) describe the isolation of a similar organism from a skin lesion of a woman who at the time harboured the usual human genital type of PPLO in her vagina.

It is difficult to decide from the evidence presented if the "G" type of Ruiter and Wentholt is a human pathogen or not. It may have some damaging effect in conjunction with a fuso-spirillary bacterial flora. However, it is of interest to note that in these lesions the same PPLO was present each time, although it differed from the common human genital PPLO type and also from the ubiquitous inhabitant of the human mouth.

The evidence presented and discussed in this chapter suggests that the human genital PPLO is indeed a potential pathogen.

# CHAPTER XI

## Conclusions and Outlook

The morphology, the methods for the growth and microscopical demonstration, the nutrition and metabolism of PPLO have been discussed in the previous chapters; other subjects such as sensitivity to various agents (including antibiotics) have been dealt with; serological and immunological reactions and results obtained therewith have been described and the pathogenicity of various organisms has been appraised. PPLO have further been compared with coccobacilliform bodies and L-forms of bacteria and the similarities and differences of organisms of the pleuropneumonia group and the two other groups mentioned have been weighed in the balance. As has been pointed out, it is the author's opinion that these three entities are different and that they can be diagnosed as distinct.

However, I should like to emphasize that neither diagnosis nor research can be carried out without expert knowledge and it is essential that an adequate training be acquired by those who wish to work in the field; many fruitful lines of research can then be pursued. Firstly, some diseases whose aetiology is as yet unknown may be caused by PPLO. Only recently it has been discovered that an inflammatory disease of swine (Switzer, 1953, 1955), a mastitis of cows (Davidson and Stuart, personal communication) and an acute septicaemia of sheep and goats in Sweden (Hanko and Otterlin, 1955) are caused by members of the pleuropneumonia group.

Studies concerning the nature of PPLO may solve the problem of their taxonomic position and their relationship to other organisms. The biochemists have found that PPLO need sterols like protozoa; they might try to find further biochemical relationships between these two groups of microbes. The similarities between PPLO and L-forms of bacteria suggest to some workers that PPLO are derived from bacteria. Further work is needed to prove or disprove this contention. If, on the other hand, we consider that PPLO produce a phase of small granules measuring not much more than 100 m$\mu$ in diameter we may regard PPLO as agents akin to viruses though they can be grown on artificial media. From this viewpoint it would be of great interest if this phase of small granules could be isolated, perhaps by means of differential centrifugation or ultra-filtration, from the bigger cells and studied morphologically and biochemically in comparison with virus particles.

In regard to problems of infection, immunity, latency and epidemiology the group of PPLO, now known to comprise many pathogens among its members, offers great possibilities for exploration. In spite of being specific with regard to their hosts and the conditions they cause, the pattern of infection produced by organisms of the group are strikingly characteristic. The organisms remain latent and hidden away in their hosts as long as the animals are healthy and not weakened by particular circumstances. As soon as other factors of an infective or noninfective nature come into action which weaken the animal or adversely affect one organ, PPLO become active and can cause grave conditions. This puzzling problem of latency deserves further study. It also seems to play a role when attempts are made to free contaminated tissue cultures from their PPLO admixtures. It is—to say the least—not easy to free the tissue cells from the PPLO without killing both, PPLO and tissue cells. After treatment it has often not been possible to isolate PPLO during the first passages, but some weeks later the same species of PPLO reappeared and could then be cultured from the tissue cells. Reinfection seems unlikely because PPLO have so far never been found as airborne contaminants. However, the reappearance of PPLO may be explained in various ways. It may be that the PPLO, weakened by the treatment designed to eradicate them, need substances which can only be provided by the living cells and are not contained in the artificial medium. Alternatively, they may survive either within or closely attached to the cells so that they cannot be separated from the latter. Further, they may have assumed a stage which allows survival only in association with living cells.

Though studied widely for practical reasons, serology has not yet been studied intensely from the theoretical point of view. We do not know the antigenic pattern of the organisms and whether the antibody response of the host is directed against surface or cytoplasmic antigens. There is wide scope for research in this field.

The workers who, in the future, will be engaged in studies of PPLO, are bound to meet with further new problems round many a corner on their way; they will not only increase our knowledge of this particular group of microorganisms but will surely also find facts of general importance.

# REFERENCES

Adler, H. E. (1960). Mycoplasma, the cause of chronic respiratory disease. *Ann. N.Y. Acad. Sci.* Art. 10, **79**, 703.

Adler, H. E., Fabricant, R., Yamamoto, R., and Berg, J. (1958). Symposium on Chronic respiratory diseases of poultry. I. Isolation and identification of pleuropneumonia-like organisms of avian origin. *Amer. J. vet. Res.* **19**, 440.

Adler, H. E., Yamamoto, R., and Berg, J. (1957). Strain differences of pleuropneumonia-like organisms of avian origin. *Avian Dis.* **1**, 19.

Almquist, E. (1922). Variations and life cycles of pathogenic bacteria. *J. infect. Dis.* **31**, 483.

"Animal Health Yearbook". (1957). Published by Food and Agricultural Organisation of the United Nations (F.A.O.) and Office Internationale des Epizooties (O.I.E.).

Bechhold, H. (1907). Kolloidstudien mit der Filtrationsmethode. *Z. phys. Chem.* **60**, 257.

Beck, S. D., and Kapadia, G. G. (1957). Insect nutrition and metabolism of sterols. *Science*, **126**, 258.

Beeuwkes, H., and Collier, W. A. (1942). Studies on arthrotropic pleuropneumonia-like organisms. *J. infect. Dis.* **70**, 1.

Berg, R. L., Daggett, W., Madden, J., and Dienes, L. (1960). The origin of PPLO in rectal cultures. *Ann. N.Y. Acad. Sci.* Art. 10, **79**, 635.

Berg, R. L., Weinberger, H., and Dienes, L. (1957). Acute hemorrhagic cystitis. *Amer. J. Med.* **22**, 848.

Beveridge, W. I. B. (1943). Isolation of pleuropneumonia-like organisms from the male urethra. *Med. J. Aust.* **2**, 479.

Beveridge, W. I. B., Campbell, A. D., and Lind, P. E. (1946). Pleuropneumonia-like organisms in cases of non-gonococcal urethritis in man and in normal female genitalia. *Med. J. Aust.* **1**, 179.

Bitter, H. (1891). Die Filtration bacterientrüber und eiweisshaltiger Flüssigkeiten durch Kieselguhrfilter. *Z. Hyg. InfektKr.* **10**, 155.

Blyth, W. A. (1958). An investigation into the aetiology of non-gonococcal urethritis with special reference to the role of pleuropneumonia-like organisms. Thesis for the degree of Doctor of Philosophy, University of London.

Bordet, J. (1910). La morphologie du microbe de la péripneumonie des bovidés. *Ann. Inst. Pasteur*, **24**, 161.

Borrel, A., Dujardin-Beaumetz E., Jeantet and Jouan. (1910). Le microbe de la péripneumonie. *Ann. Inst. Pasteur*. **24**, 168.

Brenner, S., *et al.* (1958). Bacterial protoplasts. *Nature, Lond.* **181**, 1713.

Bridré, J., and Donatien, A. (1923). Le microbe de l'agalaxie contagieuse et sa culture *in vitro*. *C. R. Acad. Sci., Paris*, **177**, 841.

Bridré, J., and Donatien, A. (1925). Le microbe de l'agalaxie contagieuse du mouton et de la chèvre. *Ann. Inst. Pasteur*, **39**, 925.

Bridré, J., Donatien, A., and Hilbert, D. (1928). Le stovarsol, spécifique de l'agalaxie contagieuse du mouton et de la chèvre. *C. R. Acad. Sci., Paris*, **187**, 262.

Briggs, S., Cranford, K., Abraham, E. P., and Gladstone, G. P. (1959). Further observations on the relationship between gram-negative rods and staphylococci grown in the presence of penicillin. *J. gen. Microbiol.*, **21**, 205.

Brown, McP. T., and Hayes, G. S. (1942). Isolation of microorganisms of the pleuropneumonia group from apparently pure cultures of the gonococcus. *J. Bact.* **43**, 82.

*Bulletins of Epizootic Diseases of Africa*. (1957). **5**, "Bureau Information": Contagious Bovine Pleuropneumonia, Distribution in Africa South of the Sahara, (1956).

Butler, M., and Knight, B. C. J. G. (1960a). The measurement of the growth of Mycoplasma in liquid media. *J. gen. Microbiol.* **22**, 478.

Butler, M., and Knight, B.C. J. G. (1960b). The survival of washed suspensions of Mycoplasma. *J. gen. Microbiol.* **22**, 470.

Butler, M., and Knight, B. C. J. G. (1960c). Steroid growth requirements and steroid growth inhibitors of Mycoplasma. *J. gen. Microbiol.* **22**, 483.

Campbell, A. D., and Turner, A. W. (1936). Complement-fixation reaction. *Bull. Coun. sci. industr. Res. Aust.* No. 97. 11.

Card, D. H. (1959). PPLO of human genital origin. Serological classification of strains and antibody distribution in man. *Brit. J. vener. Dis.* **35**, 27.

Carlson, H. J., Spector, S., and Douglas, H. G. (1951). Possible role of pleuropneumonia-like organisms in etiology of disease in childhood. *Amer. J. Dis. Child.* **81**, 193.

Carter, G. R. (1954). Pleuropneumonia-like organisms isolated from bronchopneumonia of cattle. *Science,* **120**, 113.

Carter, G. R., and McKay, K. A. (1953). A pleuropneumonia-like organism associated with infectious atrophic rhinitis of swine. *Canad. J. comp. Med.* **17**, 413.

Celli, and De Blasi (1906). Etiologia dell' agalassia contagiosa delle pecore e capre. *Ann. Igiene.* (*sper.*). fasc. 2.

Celli, and De Blasi (1906). Prima esperienza di vaccinazione contro l'agalassia contagiosa delle pecore e capre, brochure, Milan.

Chamberland. (1884). Sur un filtre donnant de l'eau physiologiquement pure. *C. R. Acad. Sci., Paris,* **99**, 247.

Cheng, K.-K. (1954). The experimental production of bronchiectasis in rats. *J. Path. Bact.* **67**, 89.

Chu, H. P. (August, 1954). The identification of infectious coryza associated with Nelson's coccobacilliform bodies in fowls in England and its similarity to the chronic respiratory disease of chickens. *Proc. the Tenth World Poultry Congress,* Edinburgh. Part III, 246

Chu, H. P. (1958a). Pleuropneumonia-like organisms and respiratory diseases of poultry. *Vet. Rec.* **70**, 55.

Chu, H. P. (1958b). Differential diagnosis and control of respiratory diseases of poultry. *Vet. Rec.* **70**, 1064.

Chu, H. P. (1960). Organisms of the pleuropneumonia group. *Vet. Annual,* **I**, 101.

Chu, H. P., and Beveridge, W. I. B. (1954). Chronic balano-posthitis in dogs associated with pleuropneumonia-like organisms. *Symposium sur les urétrites non gonococciques,* Monaco.

Chu, H. P., and Newnham, A. G. (1959). What is chronic respiratory disease of chickens ("C.R.D.")?. *Proc. XVI World Veterinary Congress,* Madrid, **I**, 163.

Collier, L. H. (1957). Contamination of stock lines of human carcinoma cells by pleuropneumonia-like organisms. *Nature, Lond.,* **180**, 757.

Conner, R. L. (1957). Interaction of stigmasterol and 2,4-dinitrophenol in the growth of *Tetrahymena pyriformis. Science,* **126**, 698.

Cordy, D. R., Adler, H. E., and Yamamoto, R. (1955). A pathogenic pleuropneumonia-like organism from goats. *Cornell. Vet.* **45**, 50.

Crawley, J. F. (1960). Use of the hemagglutination-inhibition test in the control of chronic respiratory disease of chickens. *Ann. N.Y. Acad. Sci.* **79**. Art. 10. 562.

Crawley, J. F., and Fahey, J. E. (1957). The use of the hemagglutination-inhibition test for the control of PPLO infection in poultry. *J. Amer. vet. Med. Ass.* **113**, 187.

Crowther, S., and Knight, B. C. J. G. (1956). The effect of nucleic acid fragments on the growth of a pleuropneumonia-like organism. *J. gen. Microbiol.* **14**, p.vii.

Cuckow, F. W., and Klieneberger-Nobel, E. (1955). Further studies of organisms of the pleuropneumonia group by electron microscopy. *J. gen. Microbiol.* **13**, 149.

Davies, B. D., and Dubos, R. J. (1947). The binding of fatty acids by serum albumin, a protective growth factor in bacteriological media. *J. exp. Med.* **86**, 215.

DeBlieck, L. (1942). Immunisatie tegen Coryza infectiosa Gallinarum. *Tijdschr. Diergeneesk.* **69**, 204.

DeBlieck, L. (1948). Het Tegenwoordig Standpunt inzake Coryza infectiosa Galli-narum. *Tijdschr. Diergeneesk.* **73**, 955.

DeBlieck, L. (1950). De Therapie van Coryza infectiosa Gallinarum. Type II (Nelson) met Streptomycine. *Tijdschr. Diergeneesk.* **75**, 538.

Dienes, L. (1939). "L" organism of Klieneberger and *Streptobacillus moniliformis. J. infect. Dis.* **65**, 24.

Dienes, L. (1940). Cultivation of pleuropneumonia-like organisms from female genital organs. *Proc. Soc. exp. Biol., N.Y.* **44**, 468.

Dienes, L. (1942). The significance of the large bodies and the development of L type of colonies in bacterial cultures. *J. Bact.* **44**, 37.

Dienes, L. (1945). Morphology and nature of the pleuropneumonia group of organisms. *J. Bact.* **50**, 441.

Dienes, L. (1960). Controversial aspects of the morphology of PPLO. *Ann. N.Y. Acad. Sci.* **79**, Art. 10, 356.

Dienes, L., and Edsall, J. (1937). Obesrvations on L-organisms of Klieneberger. *Proc. Soc. exp. Biol., N.Y.* **36**, 740.

Dienes, L., and Madoff, S. (1953). Differences between oral and genital strains of human pleuropneumonia-like organisms. *Proc. Soc. exp. Biol., N.Y.* **82**, 36.

Dienes, L., Ropes, N. W., Smith, W. E., Madoff, S., and Bauer, W. (1948). The role of pleuropneumonia-like organisms in genito urinary and joint diseases. *New. Engl. J. Med.* **238**, 509.

Dienes, L., and Sharp, J. T. (1955). Increased salt concentration in the isolation of L-forms of bacteria. *Bacteriol. Proc.* (Soc. Amer. Bacteriologists), **55**, 49.

Dienes, L., and Smith, W. E. (1942). Reproduction of bacteria from the large bodies of *Bacteroides funduliformis. Proc. Soc. exp. Biol., N.Y.* **51**, 297.

Dujardin-Beaumetz, E. (1900). Le microbe de la péripneumonie et sa culture. Thèse de Paris. Octave Doin, Paris, France.

Eagle, H., and Piez, K. A. (1960). The utilization of proteins by cultured human cells. *J. biol. Chem.* **235**, 1095.

Edward, D. G. ff. (1940). The occurrence in normal mice of pleuropneumonia-like organisms capable of producing pneumonia. *J. Path. Bact.* **50**, 409.

Edward, D. G. ff. (1947a). Catarrh of the upper respiratory tract in mice and its association with pleuropneumonia-like organisms. *J. Path. Bact.* **59**, 209.

Edward, D. G. ff. A selective medium for pleuropneumonia-like organisms. *J. gen. Microbiol.* **1**, 238 (1947b).

Edward, D. G. ff. (1950a). An investigation of pleuropneumonia-like organisms isolated from the bovine genital tract. *J. gen. Microbiol.* **4**, 4.

Edward, D. G. ff. (1950b). An investigation of the biological properties of organisms of the pleuropneumonia group, with suggestions regarding the identification of strains. *J. gen. Microbiol.* **4**, 311.

Edward, D. G. ff. (1952). The pleuropneumonia group of organisms and their signi-ficance in genital infection. *Brit. J. vener. Dis.* **28**, 89.

Edward, D. G. ff. (1953). A difference in growth requirements between bacteria in the L-phase and organisms of the pleuropneumonia group. *J. gen. Microbiol.* **8**, 256.

Edward, D. G. ff. (1954). The pleuropneumonia group of organisms: a review, to-gether with some new observations. *J. gen. Microbiol.* **10**, 27.

Edward, D. G. ff., and Fitzgerald, W. A. (1951a). The isolation of organisms of the pleuropneumonia group from dogs. *J. gen. Microbiol.* **5**, 566.

Edward, D. G. ff., and Fitzgerald, W. A. (1951b). Cholesterol in the growth of organisms of the pleuropneumonia group. *J. gen. Microbiol.* **5**, 576.

Edward, D. G. ff., and Fitzgerald, W. A. (1952). A growth factor needed to isolate organisms of the pleuropneumonia group from the genital tract of cattle. *Vet. Rec.* **64**, 395.

Edward, D. G. ff., and Fitzgerald, W. A. (1954). Inhibition of growth of pleuropneumonia-like organisms by antibody. *J. Path. Bact.* **68**, 23.

Edward, D. G. ff., and Freundt, E. A. (1956). The classification and nomenclature of organisms of the pleuropneumonia group. *J. gen. Microbiol.* **14**, 197.

Edward, D. G. ff., Hancock, J. L. and Hignett, S. L. (1947). Isolation of pleuropneumonia-like organisms from the bovine genital tract. *Vet. Rec.* **59**, 329.

Edwards, G. A. and Fogh, J. (1960). Fine structure of pleuropneumonia-like organisms in pure culture and in infected tissue culture cells. *J. Bact.* **79**, 267.

Elford, W. J. (1931). A new series of graded collodion membranes suitable for general bacteriological use, especially in filterable virus studies. *J. Path. Bact.* **34**, 505.

Elford, W. J. (1938). The size of viruses and bacteriophages, and the methods for their determination. *In* "Handbuch der Virusforschung" (R. Doerr and C. Hallauer, eds.), Vol. 1, p. 126. Wien.

Elford, W. J., and Andrewes, C. H. (1932). Filtration of vaccinia virus through gradocol membranes. *Brit. J. exp. Path.* **13**, 36.

Enderlein, G. (1925). "Bakteriencyclogenie". W. de Gruyter & Co., Berlin and Leipzig.

Fahey, J. E., and Crawley, J. F. (1954). Studies on chronic respiratory disease of chickens IV. A hemagglutination-inhibition diagnostic test. *Cand. J. comp. Med.* **18**, 264.

Fahey, J. E., and Crawley, J. F. (1956). Studies on chronic respiratory disease of chickens VII. The nature of infections with the pleuropneumonia-like organisms. *Cand. J. comp. Med.* **20**, 7.

Fiertel, A., and Klein, H. P. (1959). On sterols in bacteria. *J. Bact.* **78**, 738.

Findlay, G. M., Klieneberger, E., MacCallum, F. O., and Mackenzie, R. D. (1938). Rolling disease, new syndrome in mice associated with a pleuropneumonia-like organism. *The Lancet,* **ii**, 1511.

Findlay, G. M., Mackenzie, R. D., MacCallum, F. O., and Klieneberger, E. (1939). The aetiology of polyarthritis in the rat. *Lancet,* **ii**, 7.

Findlay, G. M., Mackenzie, R. D., and MacCallum, F. O. (1940). Chemotherapeutic experiments on pleuropneumonia-like organisms in rodents. *Brit. J. exp. Path.* **21**, 13.

Foster, J. P. (1934). Some historical notes on contagious pleuropneumonia. *J. Amer. vet. med. Ass.* **84**, 918.

Freundt, E. A. (1956). Occurrence and Ecology of Mycoplasma species (pleuropneumonia-like organisms) in the male urethra. *Brit. J. vener. Dis.* **32**, 188.

Freundt, E. A. (1958). "The Mycoplasmataceae (the pleuropneumonia group of organisms) Morphology, Biology and Taxonomy". Munksgaard, Copenhagen.

Freundt, E. A. (1960). Morphology and classification of PPLO. *Ann. N. Y. Acad. Sci.* **79**, Art. 10.

Gamaleia, N. (1900). Elemente der allgemeinen Bakteriologie. August Hirschwald, Berlin.

Germfree vertebrates, present status. (1959). *Ann. N. Y. Acad. Sci.* **78**, Art. 1, 1-400.

Gianforte, E. M., Jungherr, E. M., and Jacobs, R. E. (1955). A serological analysis of seven strains of pleuropneumonia-like organisms from air sac infection in poultry. *Poultry Sci.* **34**, 663.

Giesbrecht, P. (1960). Vergleichende Untersuchungen über einige Reaktionen der Chromosomen von *Bacillus megaterium* und *Amphidinium elegans*. Verhandlungen des Vierten Internationalen Kongresses für Elektronenmikroskopie. Berlin 10-17 Sept. 1958. Bd. II. Biologisch-Medizinischer Teil, Springer Verlag.

Gotthardson, A., and Melén, B. (1953). Isolation of pleuropneumonia-like organisms from ovarian abscesses. *Acta path. microbiol. scand.* **33**, 291.

Grünholz, G. (1950). Pleuropneumonieartige Mikroorganismen bei "Viruspneumonien". *Klin. Wschr.* **28**, 480.

Hadley, Ph. (1926). Microbic dissociation. *J. inf. Dis.* **40**, 1.

Hammer, A. H., Gingher, P. E., Price, R. J., and Markham, F. S. (1958). The use of the serum spot plate test for avian PPLO. *Avian Dis.* **2**, 213.

Hanko, E., and Otterlin, S. E. (1955). On an outbreak of PPLO infection in goats and sheep in Sweden. *Nord. Vet.-Med.* **7**, 609.

Harkness, A. H. (1950). Non-gonococcal urethritis. Livingstone, Edinburgh, Scotland.

Harkness, A. H., and Bushby, S. R. N. (1954). Non-gonococcal urethritis with special reference to treatment. *Wld. Hlth. Org. Rep.*, WHO/V.D.T., 117.

Harkness, A. H., and Henderson-Begg, A. (1948). The significance of pleuropneumonia-like or "L" organisms in non-gonococcal urethritis, Reiter's disease and abacterial pyuria. *Brit. J. ven. Dis.* **24**, 50.

Hayflick, L. (1960). Decontaminating tissue cultures infected with pleuropneumonia-like organisms. *Nature, Lond.* **185**, 783.

Hearn, H. J., Officer, J. E., Elsner, V. and Brown, A. (1959). Detection, elimination and prevention of contamination of cell cultures with pleuropneumonia-like organisms. *J. Bact.* **78**, 575.

Hilson, G. R. F., and Elek, S. D. (1959). An investigation into the development of gram-negative rods in penicillin-treated cultures of *Staphylococcus aureus*. *J. gen. Microbiol.* **21**, 208.

Holmes, B. E. (1937). The metabolism of the filter-passing organism "A" from sewage. *Brit. J. exp. Path.* **18**, 103.

Holmes, B. E., and Pirie, A. (1932). Growth and metabolism of the bovine pleuropneumonia virus. *Brit. J. exp. Path.* **13**, 364.

Holmgren, N. B., and Campbell, W. E. (1960). Tissue cell culture contamination in relation to bacterial-pleuropneumonia-like organisms-L-form conversion. *J. Bact.* **79**, 869.

Huijsmans-Evers, A. G. M., and Ruys, A. C. (1956a). Microorganisms of the pleuropneumonia group (Family of Mycoplasmataceae) in man. I. Cultural and biochemical characteristics. *Leeuwenhoek Ned. Tijdschr.* **22**, 371.

Huijsmans-Evers, A. G. M., and Ruys, A. C. (1956b). Microorganisms of the pleuropneumonia group (Family of Mycoplasmataceae) in man. II. Serological identification and discussion of pathogenicity. *Leeuwenhoek Ned. Tijdschr.* **22**, 377.

Iterson, W. van, and Ruys, A. C. (1960a). On the nature of PPLO. II. Electron microscopy. *Leeuwenhoek Ned. Tijdschr.* **26**, 9.

Iterson, van W., and Ruys, A. C. (1960b). The fine structure of the Mycoplasmataceae (Microorganisms of the pleuropneumonia group—PPLO). 1. Mycoplasma hominis, M. fermentans and M. salivarium. *J. Ultrastruc. Res.* **3**, 282.

Kandler, O. (1956). Vergleichende Untersuchungen über den Nukleinsäure und Atmungsstoffwechsel von *Proteus vulgaris*, dessen stabiler L-Phase und den pleuropneumonie-ähnlichen Organismen. *Zbl. Bakt.* II Abt. **109**, 335.

Kandler, G., and Kandler, O. Ernährungs- und stoffwechsel-physiologische Untersuchungen an pleuropneumonieähnlichen Organismen und der L-Phase der Bakterien. *Zbl. Bakt.* II Abt. **108**, 383 (1955).

Kandler, O., and Kandler, G. (1960). Die L-Phase der Bakterien. *Ergebn. Hyg. Bakt.* **33**, 97.

Kandler, O., and Zehender, C. (1957). Über das Vorkommen von α, ε = Diaminopimelinsäure bei verschiedenen L-Phasentypen von *Proteus vulgaris* und bei den pleuropneumonie-ähnlichen Organismen. *Z. Naturf.* **12**, 725.

Kandler, O., Zehender, C., and Müller, J. (1956a). Vergleichende Untersuchungen über den Nukleinsäuren und Atmungsstoffwechsel von *Proteus vulgaris*, dessen stabiler L-Phase und den pleuropneumonie-ähnlichen Organismen. *Arch. Mikrobiol.* **24**, 219.

Kandler, O., Zehender, C., and Müller, J. (1956b). Weitere Untersuchungen über den Atmungsstoffwechsel von *Proteus vulgaris*, dessen stabiler L-Phase und der pleuropneumonie-ähnlichen Organismen. *Arch. Mikrobiol.* **24**, 209.

Kandler, O., Hund, A., and Zehender, C. (1958). Cell wall composition in bacterial and L-forms of *Proteus vulgaris*. *Nature, Lond.* **181**, 572.

Keller, R., Smith, P. F., and Morton, H. E. (1952). Susceptibility of pleuropneumonia-like organisms from human genital tract to the action of soaps. *J. gen. Microbiol.* **7**, 313.

Kelton, W. H., Gentry, R. F., and Ludwig, E. H. (1960). Derivation of gram-positive cocci from pleuropneumonia-like organisms. *Ann. N. Y. Acad. Sci.* **79**, Art. 10, 410.

Kleckner, A. L. (1960). Serotypes of avian pleuropneumonia-like organisms. *Amer. J. vet. Res.* **21**, 274.

Klieneberger, E. (1930). Bakterienpleomorphismus und Bakterienentwicklungsgänge. *Ergebn. Hyg. Bakt.* **11**, 499.

Klieneberger, E. (1932). Ueber die Brauchbarkeit unserer Züchtungsverfahren für bakterielle Umwandlungsstudien. *Zbl. Bakt.* Abt. I **126**, 278.

Klieneberger, E. (1935). The natural occurrence of pleuropneumonia-like organisms in apparent symbiosis with *Streptobacillus moniliformis* and other bacteria. *J. Path. Bact.* **40**, 93.

Klieneberger, E. (1938). Pleuropneumonia-like organisms of diverse provenance, some results of an enquiry into methods of differentiation. *J. Hyg. Camb.* **38**, 458.

Klieneberger, E. (1939). Studies on pleuropneumonia-like organisms: The L4 organism as the cause of Woglom's pyogenic virus. *J. Hyg. Camb.* **39**, 260.

Klieneberger, E. (1940). The pleuropneumonia-like organisms: Further comparative studies and a descriptive account of recently discovered types. *J. Hyg. Camb.* **40**, 204.

Klieneberger-Nobel, E. (1949). On *Streptobacillus moniliformis* and the filtrability of its L-form. *J. Hyg. Camb.* **47**, 393.

Klieneberger-Nobel, E. (1950). Methods for the study of the cytology of bacteria and pleuropneumonia-like organisms. *Quart. J. micr. Sci.* (3rd ser.) **91**, 340.

Klieneberger-Nobel, E. (1951). Filterable forms of bacteria. *Bact. Rev.* **15**, 77.

Klieneberger-Nobel, E. (1954). Micro-organisms of the pleuropneumonia group. *Biol. Rev.* **29**, 154.

Klieneberger-Nobel, E. (1956). Über die Wesensverschiedenheit der peripneumonie-ähnlichen Organismen und der L-Phase der Bakterien. *Zbl. Bakt.* Abt. I. **165**, 329.

Klieneberger-Nobel, E. (1958). Die L-Form der Bakterien. *Zbl. Bakt.* Abt. I. **173**, 376.

Klieneberger-Nobel, E. (1959a). Pleuropneumonia-like organisms in genital infections. *Brit. med. J.* i, 19.

Klieneberger-Nobel, E. (1959b). Possible significance of PPLO in human genital infection. *Brit. J. vener. Dis.* **35**, 20.

Klieneberger-Nobel, E. (1960a). L-Forms of Bacteria. *In* "The Bacteria", Vol. I: Structure. Academic Press Inc., New York and London.

Klieneberger-Nobel, E. (1960b). Pathogenicity and immunology of organisms of the pleuropneumonia group. *Ann. N.Y. Acad. Sci.* Art. 10, **79**, 615.

Klieneberger-Nobel, E., and Cheng, K.-K. (1955). On the association of the pleuropneumonia-like L3 organism with experimentally produced bronchiectasis in rats. *J. Path. Bact.* **70**, 245.

Klieneberger-Nobel, E., and Cuckow, F. W. (1955). A study of organisms of the pleuropneumonia group by electron microscopy. *J. gen. Microbiol.* **12**, 95.

Klieneberger, E., and Smiles, J. (1942). Some observations on the developmental cycle of the organism of bovine pleuropneumonia and related microbes. *J. Hyg. Camb.* **42**, 110.

Klieneberger, E., and Steabben, D. B. (1937). On a pleuropneumonia-like organism in lung lesions of rats, with notes on the clinical, and pathological features of the underlying condition. *J. Hyg. Camb.* **37**, 143.

Klieneberger, E., and Steabben, D. B. (1940). On the association of the pleuropneumonia-like organism L3 with bronchiectatic lesions in rats. *J. Hyg. Camb.* **40**, 223.

Klinge, K. (1954). Ueber einen vom Chamaleon isolierten pleuropneumonie-ähnlichen Mikroorganismus (PPLO). *Arch. Hyg.* **138**, 332.

Knight, B. C. J. G. (1955). The principles of microbial classification. Nutritional characters. *J. gen. Microbiol.* **12**, 348.

Knöll, H. (1941). Ueber Bakterienfiltration. *Ergebn. Hyg. Bakt.* **24**, 265.

Köhler, W. (1960). Die pleuropneumonie-ähnlichen Mikroorganismen (PPLO) ("pleuropneumonia-like organisms"). Micromycetaceae. *Zbl. Bakt.* Abt. I Ref. **175**, 305.

Krücken, H. (1959). Mykoplasma species (PPLO) bei Paraurethritis. *Derm. Wschr.* **140**, 1342.

Krücken, H., and Fabry, H. (1955). Pleuropneumonia-like Organismen bei Morbus Reiter und verwandten Syndromen. *Ärztl. Wschr.* **10**, 294.

Kuhn, Ph. (1927). Die Parasiten der Bakterien. *Münch. med. Wschr.* Nr. 15.

Kuhn, Ph. (1929). Bericht über den Stand der Untersuchungen über die verschiedenen Erscheinungsformen einer Bakterienart. *Med. Klinik.* Nr. 35.

Laidlaw, P. P., and Elford, W. J. (1936). A new group of filterable organisms. *Proc. roy. Soc., B.* **120**, 292.

Leberman, P. R., Smith, P. F., and Morton, H. E. (1950). The susceptibility of pleuropneumonia-like organisms to the *in vitro* action of antibiotics: Aureomycin, chloramphenicol, dihydrostreptomycin, streptomycin, and sodium penicillin. *J. Urol.* **64**, 167.

Leberman, P. R., Smith, P. F., and Morton, H. E. (1952). Susceptibility of pleuropneumonia-like organisms to action of antibiotics. II. Terramycin and neomycin. *J. Urol.* **68**, 399.

Lecce, J. G., and Morton, H. E. (1954). Metabolic studies on three strains of pleuropneumonia-like organisms isolated from man. *J. Bact.* **67**, 62.

Lederberg, J., and St. Clair, J. (1958). Protoplasts and L-type growth of *E. coli. J. Bact.* **75**, 143.

Ledingham, J. C. G. (1933). The growth phases of pleuropneumonia and agalactia on liquid and solid media. *J. Path. Bact.* **37**, 393.

Lemcke, R. (1961). *J. Hyg. Camb.* In the press.

Ley, H. L. Jr., and Mueller, J. H. (1946). On the isolation from agar of an inhibitor for *Neisseria gonorrhoeae. J. Bact.* **52**, 453.

Liebermeister, K. (1960). Morphology of the PPLO and L-forms of proteus. *Ann. N. Y. Acad. Sci.* **79**, Art. 10, 326.

Löhnis, F. (1921). Studies upon the life cycles of the bacteria. Part I. Review of the literature 1838-1918. *Mem. nat. Acad. Sci.* **16**, 1.

Longley, E. O. (1951). Contagious caprine pleuropneumonia. A study of the disease in Nigeria. Colonial Research Publications. No. 7. H. M. Stationery Office, London.

Lynn, R. J. (1956). Nucleic acid metabolism of pleuropneumonia-like organisms. *Diss. Abst.* **16**, 1560.

Lynn, R. J. (1957). Nucleic acid metabolism in pleuropneumonia-like organisms. *Bact. Proc.* No. 126.

Lynn, R. J. (1960). Oxidative metabolism of pleuropneumonia-like organisms. *Ann. N. Y. Acad. Sci.* **79**, Art. 10, 538.

Lynn, R. J., and Morton, H. E. (1956). The inhibitory action of agar on certain strains of pleuropneumonia-like organisms. *Appl. Microbiol.* **4**, 339.

Lynn, R. J., and Smith, P. F. (1957). Nucleic acid content of pleuropneumonia-like organisms from human sources. *J. Bact.* **74**, 811.

Lynn, R. J., and Smith, P. F. (1960). Chemical composition of PPLO. *Ann. N. Y. Acad. Sci.* **79**, Art. 10, 493.

Maassen, M. (1904). Die teratologischen Wuchsformen (Involutionsformen) der Bakterien und ihre Bedeutung als diagnostisches Hilfsmittel. *Arb. Gesundh. Amt., Berl.* **21**, 385.

McKay, K. A., and Truscott, R. B. (1960). Reversion of avian pleuropneumonia-like organisms to bacteria. *Ann. N. Y. Acad. Sci.* **79**, Art. 10, 465.

Mackie, T. J., and McCartney, J. E. (1959). "Handbook of Practical Bacteriology". E. & S. Livingstone Ltd., Edinburgh, and London.

Macpherson, L. A., and Allner, K. (1960). L-forms of bacteria as contaminants in tissue culture. *Nature, Lond.* **186**, 992.

Madoff, S. (1960). Isolation and Identification of PPLO. *Ann. N. Y. Acad. Sci.* **79**, Art. 10, 383.

Mandel, P., Sensenbrenner, M., De Gregorio, P., and Bader, A. M. (1959). Distribution of nucleic acids among different stable L-forms of Proteus P 18. *Nature, Lond.* **184**, 566.

Melén, B. (1952). The susceptibility of pleuropneumonia-like organisms to the *in vitro* action of some antibiotics. *Acta path. microbiol. scand.* **30**, 98.

Melén, B., and Odeblad, E. (1951). Pleuropneumonia-like microorganisms in the female genito-urinary tract. *Scand. J. clin. Lab. Invest.* **3**, 47.

Melén, B., and Odeblad, E. (1952). Pleuropneumonia-like organisms in the genito-urinary tract of healthy women. *Acta derm. venereol. Stockh.* **32**, 74.

Melén, B., and Gotthardson, A. (1955). Complement fixation with human pleuro-pneumonia-like organisms. *Acta path. microbiol. scand.* **37**, 196.

Mellon, R. R. (1925). Studies in microbic heredity. I. Observations on a primitive form of sexuality (zygospore formation) in the colon-typhoid group. *J. Bact.* **10**, 481.

Metaxa. (1816). Quoted from Zavagli 1951.

Metchnikoff, E., Roux, E., and Salimbeni, T. (1896). Toxine et antitoxine cholériques. *Ann. Pasteur,* **10**, 257.

Miles, A. A., and Misra, S. S. (1938). The estimation of the bactericidal power of the blood. *J. Hyg. Camb.* **38**, 732.

Minck, R. (1955). Organismes du type de la péripneumonie des bovidés et formes L des bactéries. *Rev. Immunol.* **19**, 86.

Mitchell, P., and Moyle, J. (1951). The glycerophospho-protein complex envelope of *Micrococcus pyogenes. J. gen. Microbiol.* **5**, 981.

Moore, R. W., Grumbles, L. C., and Beasley, T. N. (1960). Pathological, serologic and cultural characteristics of ten avian strains of pleuropneumonia-like organisms. *Ann. N. Y. Acad. Sci.* **79**, Art. 10, 556.

Mooser, H. (1945). Einschlusskörper und Entwicklungsstadien bei Rickettsien. *Experientia,* **I**, 336.

Mooser, H. (1949). Die Mobilisation von Musculomyces durch das Virus der Ektromelia. *Experientia,* **5**, 364.

Mooser, H. (1951). Two varieties of murine PPLO strains distinguishable from each other by their mode of *in vivo* growth when associated with the virus of ectromelia. *Arch. ges. Virusforsch.* **4**, 207.

Mooser, H., and Joos, H. (1952). Die Infektion der Maus mit menschlichen PPLO-stämmen. *Schweiz. Z. allg. Path.* **15**, 735.

Morton, H. E., and Lecce, J. G. (1953). Selective action of thallium acetate and crystal violet for pleuropneumonia-like organisms of human origin. *J. Bact.* **66**, 646.

Morton, H. E., Smith, P. F., and Leberman, P. R. (1949). Symbiotic growth of pleuropneumonia-like organisms with bacterial colonies. *Proc. Soc. exp. Biol. N. Y.* **72**, 328.

Morton, H. E., Smith, P. F., Williams, N. B., and Eickenberg, C. F. (1951). Isolation of pleuropneumonia-like organisms from human saliva: a newly detected member of the oral flora. *J. dent. Res.* **30**, 415.

Nasemann, T., Röckl, H., and Huber, O. (1954). Die pleuropneumonie-ähnlichen Organismen. Verhalten in der Eikultur und im Resistenzversuch. *Klin. Wschr.* **32**, 717.

Nasemann, T., and Röckl, H. (1960). Pleuropneumonia-like organisms: their effect on chicken chorioallantoic membrane and their resistance to antibiotics. *Ann. N. Y. Acad. Sci.* **79**, Art. 10, 588.

Neimark, H. C., and Pickett, M. J. (1960). Products of glucose metabolism by pleuropneumonia-like organisms. *Ann. N. Y. Acad. Sci.* **79**, Art. 10, 531.

Neisser, M. (1926). Ueber Gärung. *Zbl. Bakt.* **97**, 14.

Nelson, J. B. (1935). Coccobacilliform bodies associated with an infectious fowl coryza. *Science*, **82**, 43.

Nelson, J. B. (1936a). Studies on an uncomplicated coryza of the domestic fowl. V. A coryza of slow onset. *J. exp. Med.* **63**, 509.

Nelson, J. B. (1936b). Studies on an uncomplicated coryza of the domestic fowl. VI. Coccobacilliform bodies in birds infected with the coryza of slow onset. *J. exp. Med.* **63**, 515.

Nelson, J. B. (1936c). Studies on an uncomplicated coryza of the domestic fowl. VII. Cultivation of the coccobacilliform bodies in fertile eggs and in tissue culture. *J. exp. Med.* **64**, 749.

Nelson, J. B. (1936d). Studies on an uncomplicated coryza of the domestic fowl. VIII. The infectivity of fetal membrane and tissue culture suspensions of the coccobacilliform bodies. *J. exp. Med.* **64**, 759.

Nelson, J. B. (1937a). Infectious catarrh of mice. I. A natural outbreak of the disease. *J. exp. Med.* **65**, 833.

Nelson, J. B. (1937b). Infectious catarrh of mice. II. The detection and isolation of coccobacilliform bodies. *J. exp. Med.* **65**, 843.

Nelson, J. B. (1937c). Infectious catarrh of mice. III. The etiological significance of the coccobacilliform bodies. *J. exp. Med.* **65**, 851.

Nelson, J. B. (1939). Growth of the fowl coryza bodies in tissue culture and in blood agar. *J. exp. Med.* **69**, 199.

Nelson, J. B. (1940a). Infectious catarrh of the albino rat. I. Experimental transmission in relation to the role of *Actinobacillus muris*. *J. exp. Med.* **72**, 645.

Nelson, J. B. (1940b). Infectious catarrh of the albino rat. II. The causal relation of coccobacilliform bodies. *J. exp. Med.* **72**, 655.

Nelson, J. B. (1948). The nasal transmission of pleuropneumonia-like organisms in mice and rats. *J. inf. Dis.* **82**, 169.

Nelson, J. B. (1949a). Observations on a pneumotropic virus obtained from wild rats. I. Transmission of the agent to white mice and rats. *J. inf. Dis.* **84**, 21.

Nelson, J. B. (1949b). Observations on a pneumotropic virus obtained from wild rats. II. Biological characteristics of the agent. *J. inf. Dis.* **84**, 26.

Nelson, J. B. (1960). Discussion remark. *Ann. N. Y. Acad. Sci.* Art. 10, **79**, 460.

Nicol, C. S., and Edward, D. G.ff. (1953). Role of organisms of the pleuropneumonia group in human genital infections. *Brit. J. vener. Dis.* **29**, 141.

Nocard, E., and Roux, E. R. (1898), avec la collaboration de M. M. Borrel, Salimbeni et Dujardin-Beaumetz. Le microbe de la péripneumonie. *Ann. Inst. Pasteur*, **12**, 240.

Nordtmeyer, H. (1891). Ueber Wasserfiltration durch Filter aus gebrannter Infusorienerde. *Z. Hyg. Infektkr.* **10**, 145.

Oates, J. K., Whittington, M. J. and Wilkinson, A. E. (1959). A note on the results of cultural and serological tests for pleuropneumonia-like organisms in Reiter's disease. *Brit. J. vener. Dis.* **35**, 184.

Paine, T. F., Jr., and Daniel, R. R. (1959). Attempts to obtain gram-negative rods from staphylococci treated with penicillin. *J. gen. Microbiol.* **21**, 203.

Panos, C., Barkulis, S. S., and Hayashi, J. A. (1960). Streptococcal L-forms. III. Effect of sonic treatment on viability. *J. Bact.* **80**, 336.

Partridge, S. M., and Klieneberger, E. (1941). Isolation of cholesterol from the oily droplets found in association with the L1 organism separated from *Streptobacillus moniliformis*. *J. Path. Bact.* **52**, 219.

Peoples, D. M., Morton, H. E., and Feo, L. G. (1957). Unusual pleuropneumonia-like organism isolated in a study of *Trichomonas vaginalis* from cases of chronic urethritis. *J. Bact.* **73**, 398.

Pirie, A. (1938). The effect of catalase on the respiration of a filterable organism from sewage. *Brit. J. exp. Path.* **19**, 9.

Pirie, A., and Holmes, B.E. (1933). A study of the enzymes of the agalactia virus. *Brit. J. exp. Path.* **14**, 290.

Pigoury, L. (1938). L'Agalaxie contagieuse de la chèvre au Liban. *Bull. Soc. Path. exot.* **31**, 194.

Plackett, P. (1957). Depolymerisation of ribonucleic acid by extracts of *Asterococcus mycoides*. *Biochim. biophys. Acta*, **26**, 664.

Plackett, P. (1959). On the probable absence of "muco-complex" from *Mycoplasma mycoides*. *Biochim. biophys. Acta*, **35**, 260.

Plackett, P., and Buttery, S. H. (1958). A galactan from *Mycoplasma mycoides*. *Nature, Lond.* **182**, 1236.

Pollock, M. R. (1949). The effects of long-chain fatty acids on the growth of *Haemophilus pertussis* and other organisms. *Symp. Soc. exp. Biol.* **3**, 193.

Prausnitz, P. H. (1930). Kolloidtechn. Sammelreferat. XVIII. Filtration im Laboratorium. *Kolloid-Z.* **50**, 77, 167.

Priestley, F. W., and White, R. W. (1952). A note on the isolation, from serum, of a heat-stable growth factor for the contagious bovine pleuro-pneumonia organism. *Vet. Rec.* **64**, 259.

Provost, A., and Villemot, J. M. (1959). Recherches immunologiques sur la péripneumonie. IV. A propos du diagnostic de laboratoire de la pleuropneumonie contagieuse caprine. *Rev. Elev.* **12**, 11.

Razin, S., and Knight, B. C. J. G. (1960a). A partially defined medium for the growth of Mycoplasma. *J. gen. Microbiol.* **22**, 1492.

Razin, S., and Knight, B. C. J. G. (1960b). The effects of ribonucleic acid and deoxyribonucleic acid on the growth of Mycoplasma. *J. gen. Microbiol.* **22**, 504.

Razin, S., and Oliver, O. (1961). Morphogenesis of Mycoplasma and bacterial L-form colonies. *J. gen. Microbiol.* **24**, 225.

Réunion sur les Formes L. (1957) *Nature, Lond.* **179**, 461.

Robinson, L. B., Wichelhausen, R. A., and Brown, T. McP. (1952). Sensitivity studies on human pleuropneumonia-like organisms. *J. Lab. clin. Med.* **39**, 290.

Robinson, L. B., Wichelhausen, R. H., and Roizman, B. (1956). Contamination of human cell cultures by PPLO. *Science*, **124**, 1147.

Rodwell, A. W. (1956). The role of serum in the nutrition of *Asterococcus mycoides*. *Aust. J. biol. Sci.* **9**, 105.

Rodwell, A. W. (1960a). Nutrition and metabolism of *Mycoplasma mycoides* var. mycoides. *Ann. N. Y. Acad. Sci.* Art. 10, **79**, 499.

Rodwell, A. W. (1960b). Discussion of part IV. *Ann. N. Y. Acad. Sci.* **79**, Art. 10, 551.

Rodwell, A. W., and Rodwell, E. S. (1953). Pathway for glucose oxidation in *Asterococcus mycoides*. *Nature, Lond.* **172**, 254.

Rodwell, A. W., and Rodwell, E. S. (1954a). The breakdown of carbohydrates by *Asterococcus mycoides*, the organism of bovine pleuropneumonia. *Aust. J. biol. Sci.* **7**, 18.

Rodwell, A. W., and Rodwell, E. S. (1954b). The breakdown of pyruvate by *Asterococcus mycoides*, the organism of bovine pleuropneumonia. *Aust. J. biol. Sci.* **7**, 31.

Rodwell, A. W., and Rodwell, E. S. (1954c). The pathway for glucose oxidation by *Asterococcus mycoides*, the organism of bovine pleuropneumonia. *Aust. J. biol. Sci.* **7**, 37.

Rothblat, G. H., and Morton, H. E. (1958). The detection of contaminating pleuro-pneumonia-like organisms (PPLO) in cultures of tissue cells. *Bacteriol. Proc.* **58**, 73.

Roux, J. (1960). La multiplication des formes L. *Ann. Inst. Pasteur*, **99**, 286.

Rubin, A. N. L., Somerson, P. E., Smith, P. F., and Morton, H. E. (1954). The effects of the administration of erythromycin upon Neisseria gonorrhea and pleu-ropneumonia-like organisms in the uterine cervix. *Am. J. Syph.* **38**, 472.

Ruiter, M., and Wentholt, H. M. M. (1950). Isolation of a pleuropneumonia-like organism in primary fusospirochaetal gangrene of the penis. *J. Invest. Dermat.* **15**, 301.

Ruiter, M., and Wentholt, H. M. M. (1952). The occurrence of a pleuropneu-monia-like organism in fusospirillary infections of the human genital mucosa. *J. Invest. Dermat.* **18**, 313.

Ruiter, M., and Wentholt, H. M. M. (1953a). Isolation of a pleuropneumonia-like organism (G-strain) in a case of fusospirillary vulvovaginitis. *Acta derm.-venereol. Stockh.* **33**, 123.

Ruiter, M., and Wentholt, H. M. M. (1953b). Incidence, significance and bacteriolo-gical features of pleuropneumonia-like organisms in a number of pathological conditions of the human genito-urinary tract. *Acta derm.-venereol. Stockh.* **33**, 130.

Ruiter, M., and Wentholt, H. M. M. (1955). Isolation of a pleuropneumonia-like organism from a skin lesion associated with a fusospirochaetal flora. *J. Invest. Dermat.* **24**, 31.

Ruska, H., and Poppe, K. (1947). Elektronenmikroskopische Untersuchungen zur Morphologie der Seiffertschen Mikroorganismen und des Erregers der Lungen-seuche des Rindes. *Z. Hyg. InfektKr.* **127**, 201.

Ruys, A. C. (1960). On the nature of PPLO. I. Bacteriological observations. *Leeuwenhoek Ned. Tijdschr.* **26**, 1.

Sabin, A. B. (1938a). Isolation of a filtrable, transmissible agent with "neurolytic" properties from toxoplasma infected tissues. *Science*, **88**, 189.

Sabin, A. B. (1938b). Identification of the filtrable, transmissible neurolytic agent isolated from toxoplasma-infected tissue as a new pleuropneumonia-like microbe. *Science*, **88**, 575.

Sabin, A. B. (1941). The filtrable microorganisms of the pleuropneumonia group. *Bact. Rev.* **5**, 1.

Sabin, A. B., and Johnson, B. (1940). Pathogenic pleuropneumonia-like micro-organisms in tissues of normal mice, an isolation of new immunological types. *Proc. Soc. exp. Biol. N. Y.* **44**, 569.

Sabin, A. B., and Warren, J. (1940). The therapeutic effectiveness of a practically non-toxic new compound (calcium aurothiomalate) in experimental, prolifera-tive chronic arthritis of mice. *Science*, **92**, 535.

Salaman, M. H. (1946). The isolation of organisms of the pleuropneumonia group from the genital tract and their relation to the gonococcus. *Brit. J. vener. Dis.* **22**, 47.

Salaman, M. H., and Collaborators. (1946). The isolation of organisms of the pleuro-pneumonia group from the genital tract of men and women. *J. Path. Bact.* **58**, 31.

Schauwecker, R. (1947). Untersuchungen über einen dem Erreger der Pleuropneu-monia ähnlichen Mikroorganismus in der weissen Maus. *Schweiz. Z. Path.* **10**, 714.

Schmidt-Kehl, L. (1930). Der Formwechsel der Sarzinen. Erste Mitteilung (Kon-stantes Auftreten von gramnegativen Stäbchen). *Arch. Hyg. Berl.* **103**, 235.

Schröder, H., and Dusch, Th. v. (1854). Ueber Filtration der Luft in Beziehung auf Fäulnis und Gärung. *Ann. Chem. u. Pharmaz.* **89**, 232.

Seddon, H. R. (1953). "Diseases of Domestic Animals in Australia". Part 5, Vol. II: Bacterial Diseases, Contagious Bovine Pleuropneumonia.

Seiffert, G. (1937a). Ueber das Vorkommen filtrabler Mikroorganismen in der Natur und ihre Züchtbarkeit. *Zbl. Bakt.* I. Abt. Orig., **139**, 337.

Seiffert, G. (1937b). Filtrable Mikroorganismen in der freien Natur. *Zbl. Bakt.* Abt. I. Orig. Beiheft. **140**, 168.

Sharp, J. T. (1954). L-colonies from hemolytic streptococci: new technic in the study of L-forms of bacteria. *Proc. Soc. exp. Biol. N. Y.* **87**, 94.

Shepard, M. C. (1956). T-form colonies of pleuropneumonia-like organisms. *J. Bact.* **71**, 362.

Shepard, M. C. (1957) Visualisation and morphology of pleuropneumonia-like organisms in clinical material. *J. Bact.* **73**, 162.

Shepard, M. C. (1958). Growth and development of T-strain pleuropneumonia-like organisms in human epidermoid carcinoma cells. (HeLa). *J. Bact.* **75**, 351.

Shoetensack, H. M. (1934). Pure cultivation of the filtrable virus isolated from canine distemper. *Kitasato Arch.* **11**, 277.

Shoetensack, H. M. (1936a). Pure cultivation of filtrable virus isolated from canine distemper (Part II). Morphological and cultural features of *Asterococcus canis*, Type I, n.sp. and *Asterococcus canis*, Type II, n.sp. *Kitasato Arch.* **13**, 175.

Shoetensack, H. M. (1936b). Studies concerning the relation between canine distemper and *Asterococcus canis* Type I and II. *Kitasato Arch.* **13**, 269.

Skeggs, H. R., Spizizen, J., and Wright, L. D. (1950). Competitive antagonism of ribonucleic and desoxyribonucleic acids in the nutrition of *Lactobacillus bifidus*. *J. Amer. chem. Soc.* **72**, 811.

Smith, P. F. (1955a). Synthetic media for pleuropneumonia-like organisms. *Proc. Soc. exp. Biol. N. Y.* **88**, 628.

Smith, P. F. (1955b). Amino acid metabolism by pleuropneumonia-like organisms. I. General catabolism. *J. Bact.* **70**, 552.

Smith, P. F. (1956). Quantitative measurement of the growth of pleuropneumonia-like organisms. *Appl. Microbiol.* **4**, 254.

Smith, P. F. (1957a). Amino acid metabolism by pleuropneumonia-like organisms. II. Glutamine. *J. Bact.* **73**, 91.

Smith, P. F. (1957b). Amino acid metabolism by pleuropneumonia-like organisms. Glutamic acid. *J. Bact.* **74**, 75.

Smith, P. F. (1957c). Conversion of citrulline to ornithine by pleuropneumonia-like organisms. *J. Bact.* **74**, 801.

Smith, P. F. (1959). Cholesterol esterase activity of pleuropneumonia-like organisms. *J. Bact.* **77**, 682.

Smith, P. F. (1960a). Nutritional requirements of PPLO and their relation to metabolic function. *Ann. N. Y. Acad. Sci.* **79**, Art. 10, 508.

Smith, P. F. (1960b). Amino acid metabolism of PPLO. *Ann. N. Y. Acad. Sci.* Art. 10, **79**, 543.

Smith, P. F., Lecce, J. G., and Lynn, R. J. (1954). A lipoprotein as a growth factor for certain pleuropneumonia-like organisms. *J. Bact.* **68**, 627.

Smith, P. F., and Lynn, R. J. (1958). Lipid requirements for the growth of pleuropneumonia-like organisms. *J. Bact.* **76**, 264.

Smith, P. F., Morton, H. E., and Leberman, P. R. (1950). Susceptibilities of pleuropneumonia-like organisms to some selective bacteriostatic agents. *Proc. Soc. exp. Biol. N. Y.* **74**, 552.

Smith, P. F., and Morton, H. E. (1951a). Isolation of pleuropneumonia-like organisms from the throats of humans. *Science*, **113**, 623.

Smith, P. F., and Morton, H. E. (1951b). The separation and characterization of the growth factor in serum and ascitic fluid which is required by certain pleuropneumonia-like organisms. *J. Bact.* **61**, 395.

Smith, P. F., and Morton, H. E. (1952). Further characterization of the protein factor required by certain pleuropneumonia-like organisms for growth *in vitro*. *Arch. Biochem. Biophys.* **38**, 23.

Smith, P. F., and Morton, H. E. (1953). Nature of growth inhibitor in some mammalian sera for pleuropneumonia-like organisms of human origin. *Proc. Soc. exp. Biol. N. Y.* **83**, 65.

Smith, P. F., Peoples, D. M., and Morton, H. E. (1957). Conversion of pleuropneumonia-like organisms to bacteria. *Proc. Soc. exp. Biol. N. Y.* **96**, 550.

Smith, P. F., and Sasaki, S. (1958). Stability of pleuropneumonia-like organisms to some physical factors. *Appl. Microbiol.* **6**, 184.

Somerson, N. L. (1954). Deamination by pleuropneumonia-like organisms. *Bact. Proc.* p. 30.

Somerson, N. L., and Morton, H. E. (1953). Reduction of tetrazolium salts by pleuropneumonia-like organisms. *J. Bact.* **65**, 245.

Stokes, E. J. (1955). Human infection with pleuropneumonia-like organisms. *Lancet*, **i**, 276.

Sullivan, E. R., and Dienes, L. (1939). Pneumonia in white mice produced by a pleuro-pneumonia-like micro-organism. *Proc. Soc. exp. Biol. N. Y.* **41**, 620.

Swift, H. F., and Brown, T. McP. (1939). Pathogenic pleuropneumonia-like microorganisms from acute rheumatic exudates and tissues. *Science*, **89**, 271.

Switzer, W. P. (1953). Studies on infectious rhinitis of swine. I. Isolation of a filterable agent from the nasal cavity of swine with infectious atrophic rhinitis. *J. Amer. vet. med. Ass.* **123**, 45.

Switzer, W. P. (1955). Studies on infectious atrophic rhinitis of swine. IV. Characterization of a pleuropneumonia-like organism isolated from the nasal cavities of swine. *Amer. J. vet. Res.* **16**, 540.

Talalay, P., Hurlock, B., and Williams-Ashman, H. G. (1958). On the coenzymatic function of estradiol-17 beta. *Proc. nat. Acad. Sci. Wash.* **44**, 862.

Tang, F. F., Wei, H., McWhirter, D. L., and Edgar, J. (1935). An investigation of the causal agent of bovine pleuropneumonia. *J. Path. Bact.* **40**, 391.

Thorsson, K. G., and Weibull, C. (1958). Electron microscopy of a stable Proteus L-form. *Nature, Lond.* **181**, 1348.

Tourtellotte, M. E., and Jacobs, R. E. (1960). Physiological and serologic comparisons of PPLO from various sources. *Ann. N. Y. Acad. Sci.* **79**, Art. 10, 521.

Turner, A. W. (1935). A study on the morphology and life cycles of the organism of pleuropneumonia contagiosa boum (*Borrelomyces peripneumoniae* nov. gen) by observation in the living state under dark-ground illumination. *J. Path. Bact.* **41**, 1.

Turner, A. W. (1959). Pleuro-pneumonia group of diseases. *In* "Infectious Diseases of Animals" (A. W. Stableforth and L. A. Galloway, eds.), Vol. 2: Diseases Due to Bacteria, pp. 437-480. Butterworths Scientific Publications, London.

Villemot, J. M., and Provost, A. (1959a). Recherches immunologiques sur la péripneumonie. III. Isolement au Tchad de PPLO génitaux d'origine bovine. *Rev. Elev.* **12**, 5.

Villemot, J. M., and Provost, A. (1959b). Recherches immunologiques sur la péripneumonie. V. Relations antigéniques entre mycoplasma mycoides var mycoides, M. mycoides var, capri et d'autres micro-organismes du genre Mycoplasma. *Rev. Elev.* **12**, 251.

Villemot, J. M., and Provost, A. (1959c). Recherches immunologiques sur la péripneumonie. VI. Bases d'une classification sérologique des micro-organismes du genre Mycoplasma. *Rev. Elev.* **12**, 369.

Villemot, J. M., and Provost, A. (1960). Isolement au Tchad de micro-organismes du groupe de la péripneumonie appartenant à l'espèce Mycoplasma (*Asterococcus hominis*). *Ann. Inst. Pasteur*, **99**, 114.

Wagtendonk, W. J. van (1955). The nutrition of ciliates. Biochemistry and Physiology of Protozoa. Eds. S. H. Hutner and A. Lwoff. Academic Press Inc. New York, **2**, 57-84.

Warren, J. (1942). Observations on some biological characteristics of organisms of the pleuropneumonia group. *J. Bact.* **43**, 211.

Warthin, J. A. (1948). Reiter's syndrome. A report on four patients treated with streptomycin. *Amer. J. Med.* **4**, 827.

Weibull, C. (1958). Chemical analyses elucidating the structure of bacterial L-forms. *Acta path. microbiol. scand.* **42**, 324.

Weibull, C., and Beckman, H. (1960a). Growth of bacterial L-forms and bacterial protoplasts. *J. Bact.* **79**, 638.

Weibull, C., and Beckman, H. (1960b). Metabolism of small bodies isolated from a stable Proteus L-form. *Nature, Lond.* **188**, 428.

Wentholt, H. M. M. (1952). Voorkomen van pleuropneumonie-achtige Organismen bij urogenitale Ontstekingsprocessen. Thesis, Groningen, Holland

Whittlestone, P. (1957). Some respiratory diseases of pigs. *Vet. Rec.* **69**, 1354.

Willems, quoted from Dujardin-Baumetz, Thèse, Paris (1900).

Wilson, G. S. (1959). Faults and fallacies in microbiology. *J. gen. Microbiol.* **21**, 1.

Witt, C. (1925). Die Lungenseuche und ihre leichte, schnelle Heilbarkeit. *Berl. tierärztl. Wschr.* **41**, 369.

Wittler, R. G., Cary, S. G., and Lindberg, R. B. (1956). Reversion of a pleuropneumonia-like organism to a corynebacterium during tissue culture passage. *J. gen. Microbiol.* **14**, 763.

Woglom, W. H., and Warren, J. (1938a). A pyogenic virus in the rat. *Science*, **87**, 370.

Woglom, W. H., and Warren, J. (1938b). A pyogenic filterable agent in the albino rat. *J. exp. Med.* **68**, 513.

Woglom, W. H., and Warren, J. (1939). The nature of a pyogenic filterable agent in the white rat. *J. Hyg. Camb.* **39**, 266.

Yamamoto, R., and Adler, H. E. (1958). Characterization of pleuropneumonia-like organisms of avian origin. I. Antigenic analysis of seven strains and their comparative pathogenicity for birds. *J. infect. Dis.* **102**, 143.

Zavagli, V. (1951). L'agalaxie contagieuse des brebis et des chèvres. Office Internationale des Epizooties. Rapport à la XIX session, R. No. 201.

Zehender, C. (1956). Vergleichende Untersuchungen über die Wirkung von Atmungsgiften auf pleuropneumonie-ähnliche Organismen, *Proteus vulgaris* und dessen stabile μ L-Phase. *Zbl. Bakt.* Abt. II. **109**, 337.

# Author Index

Numbers in italics indicate the page on which the reference is listed

## A

# Subject Index

## A

Agalactia of sheep and goats, 7
  discovery and culture of agent of, 8
  distribution of, 9
  experimental infection with agent of, 9
  lesions (eyes, joints, mammae) caused
    by, 8
  vaccination against, 9
Amino acids in PPLO, 97
  breakdown of, 98
  catabolism of, 98
  metabolism of, 98
  requirements for, 97
Antibiotics, 108
  inhibition of PPLO by (reports of
    various workers), 110
  sensitivity of human genital type
    PPLO to, 109
  therapeutic effect of, 111
Antibodies in the blood of the host, 117
  cattle, 5
  chickens, 118
  rats, 118
  mice, 120
  human beings (various groups), 121,
    133

## B

Bronchiectasis (bronchopneumonia) in
    rats, 13
  following ligation of bronchus, 14, 123
  occurrence at different ages, 40, 57
  organism of, 58
  pathology, 14
  serological study of, 15
  symptoms, 13

## C

Carbohydrates, 99
  metabolism, 99, 100
    under anaerobic conditions, 101
  requirements, 99
Chemical composition of pleuropneu-
    monia-like organisms, 91, 92
Coccobacilliform bodies (chicken),
    69–73
  characteristics of, 70

comparison with PPLO, 71
  definition of
    by growth characteristics, 69
    by morphological features, 69
  differential diagnosis of chicken-coc-
    cobacilliform bodies from
    chicken-PPLO, 73
  discovery of, 69
  pathogenicity of, 71
  occurrence of, in rats and mice, 73
Colonies of pleuropneumonia-like or-
    ganisms, 27, 28, 29
  deceptive appearance of, 87, 88

## F

Filtration of pleuropneumonia-like or-
    ganisms and L-forms, 61
  historical introduction, 61
  ultrafiltration analysis, 62
    calculation of particle size, 63
    filters available for, 62, 63
    PPLO and L-forms applied to, 63
    filters, 64
    methods, 64
    organisms, 64
    results, 65

## G

Growth factors, 92
  requirements for, 104

## H

Human infections, 124
  significance of PPLO in non-gonococ-
    cal urethritis, 124
    identification of strains, 127
    media recommended, 125, 126
    taking of specimens, 127
    transport and transfer of specimens
      to media, 127
    selection of cases for study, 128–131
  non-gonococcal urethritis, conditions
    other than, 131

## I

Isolation of pleuropneumonia-like or-
    ganisms, 57–60